Life Finds A Way

Copyright © Cynthia F. Ambriz

First Edition

ISBN (paperback) [978-1-914447-57-0]

ISBN (ebook) [978-1-914447-58-7]

D1604284

Book Design by TGH International Ltd

Photos by Cynthia F. Ambriz

Prepared by TGH International Ltd., Whitehall House, Leicester,
United Kingdom, LE19 4SD

www.TGHBooks.com

Life Finds A Way

A Journey of Healing and A Return to Wholeness

Cynthia F. Ambriz

Contents

Acknowledgments

I would like to say thank you to my Son Michael for agreeing to play the role of teacher for me in this lifetime. His wisdom has been something I have appreciated and learned from over the years and for that I am grateful. Thank you to his amazing wife and my daughter in love Genesis for sharing her love so freely with us. Thank you to my granddaughter Natasha, for coming into my life and implementing necessary changes and not asking for permission. She came at just the right time and her Nana thanks her. Thank you to my granddaughter Makaira for bringing so much joy into our lives and allowing me to witness her entry into this lifetime. We are incredibly blessed by your presence.

Thank you to my mother Bertha and my father Guillermo. Although this life was incredibly challenging at times, I attribute so much of who I have become to you providing me with the perfect set of circumstances. You agreed to play these roles for me, and I will forever be grateful to you. Thank you to my brother Juan Carlos and my sister Aide for also agreeing to play these roles in this nail-biting saga called our lives. I love you and honor the Christ in you.

I want to thank my husband, and best friend, Jesse. You challenge me to question whether my positions are still accurate. You reveal to me what still needs healing. And through it all, you never stop loving me. Thank you for your unwavering love, support and encouragement to be more me.

Thank you to my teacher Rev. Michael B. Beckwith for allowing the Agape International Spiritual Center to come into existence through him. The day I arrived at Agape, I knew I was home. Thank you for the years of teachings, love, and support that allowed me to awaken to the truth of my being.

Thank you to my teacher Dr. Sue Morter whose teachings also arrived at just the right time. I had no idea prior to meeting Dr. Sue that I was not living in my body and how necessary that would be to access more of my real self. Through her work on embodiment, I am living the life God created me for in the first place.

Thank you to the Agape Practitioner Core. These individuals held a space of unwavering life as I died to my old self, over and over again. Thank you for your unconditional love and for the years of support, guidance, and inspiration.

Thank you, Karen Mills-Alston, for reaching out to me and "encouraging" me to finish this book. You are such a powerful example of what a woman of integrity who loves God looks like, and I thank God for you.

Thank you Akili Beckwith, my Spiritual Practitioner, for listening to me tell you my story one experience at a time and always holding the truth about me and all involved while simultaneously allowing me to cry and heal.

Thank you Rev. Cheryl D. Ward for showing up in my dreams before showing up in physical form and allowing me to know I was in the right place at the right time. Your "Self Awareness" class gave me permission to begin to release the many masks I had worn throughout the years and begin to explore what it meant to be me.

Thank you to all of the individuals that have played a role in my life. I could not have done any of this without you. Whether we speak regularly or simply allow a smile to come over our faces when we think of each other, know I love you, no matter what it looks like in the human drama.

Thank you to God for creating me and entrusting me with my sacred life. Thank you to Mother Mary for making yourself known to me early on. Thank you, Yeshua for allowing me to be here on Earth and remembering my sacred origins through it all. I thank you, and I love you, and I know we work together for the good of humanity.

- Cynthia F. Ambriz

Praise from Michael Bernard Beckwith

What is healing, and how do we heal?

Metaphysically speaking, as Spiritual beings, to heal is to simply become consciously aware of — and embody — our innate perfection, wholeness, and oneness. To intentionally bring our focus and attention back to that Truth by transcending the mental habits of believing in lack, limitation, and separation, and having feelings of not being loved, lovable, worthy, or enough. To utilize the spiritual tools and technologies of meditation, affirmative prayer, and spiritual study so that we become aligned with our Divine nature and identity. We heal by healing the inner perceptual divide. We heal by remembering Who We Are.

Each of us, in one way or another, is on a journey of, to, and through healing. Although at the core the cause and solution to healing are found, the way your path to healing expresses does vary and is based solely on the curriculum you registered for before incarnating to Earth. If you want to know your curriculum, just observe the areas that trigger and elicit a deep response and reaction from you. That will point you in the right direction, it will show you the way.

Life Finds a Way' details one soul's journey to healing and deep remembrance. Rev. Cynthia, or Cyndi as we used to call her at Agape International Spiritual Center, gives a transparent account of her journey to healing and allows us access to her unique curriculum, the soul classes she has signed up for, and the tests she had to take (and sometimes retake). She bravely bares and recounts pivotal moments—some that will make you shake your head, widen your eyes, cringe, and sometimes even squirm with discomfort and disbelief — with levity and humor.

Rev. Cynthia doesn't hold back and doesn't blame; she takes full responsibility for her life and everything that unfolded. Thist self-responsibility is an indicator of self-mastery, self-knowledge, and self-love — three qualities that we strengthen during our healing journey.

Life Finds a Way' is a beautiful reminder that despite even the most debilitating, crushing, hopeless, and disempowering experiences and situations, everything serves to lead us home: home to self, home to Truth, home to oneness, and home to love.

Enjoy your journey,

- *Michael Bernard Beckwith*. Founder & CEO, Agape International Spiritual Center. Author of *Life Visioning* and *Spiritual Liberation*.

Praise from Rev. Dr Julie Moret

Every once in a while, someone comes along whose very presence commands attention. Rev Cynthia Ambriz is just that person. I noticed her immediately, over five years ago, when she walked into my public speaking course at the Michael B. Beckwith School of Ministry. At first glance she seemed shy and reserved, but I was not fooled. Cynthia is a dynamic powerhouse - an insightful, wise, Teflon-strong mystic whose story confirms that whatever you are moving through, she's got the tools and practices to guide you to the other side.

In *'Life Finds a Way'* Rev Cyndi shares many of these time-tested practices honed through her own experiences and proves, truly, that *life finds a way*.

With each page of her captivating story, Cyndi makes three things abundantly clear:

1. You are not alone.
2. Healing and transformation are possible.
3. Life never gives up on us. It finds a way. Your life has done exactly that by leading you to this exceptional road map for health and healing.

Blessings on your journey,

*- **Rev Dr Julie Moret**.* Author of *What's Your What, How to Ignite Your Unique Brand.*

A Note From The Author

First of all, thank you for picking up this book. It is no accident you are reading it at this moment in time. The purpose of this book is multi faceted. As you read my story, I share with you how I went about trying to heal and in the process, discovered that what needs healing may go beyond the physical body. In fact, what I learned is that everything begins in our energy bodies before it ever shows up in the physical.

Considering that I carried unprocessed trauma and emotions for years before I began to share it with anyone, I am not surprised it ultimately expressed itself as a condition. The autoimmune condition I have is one in which the immune system attacks my body, specifically my motor nerves. This has caused me to slow down and begin to pay attention to what my needs are, and it has kept me mindful of how I am feeling on a consistent basis. If the condition had a face, I imagine it to look like a guardian angel. It has been present with me for the past twenty years and has served as a catalyst for healing on every level.

I do not share my story lightly. In fact, when I first tried to write this truth in 2018, it felt like I was spewing venom onto the computer screen through my fingers. As I have saught to heal, I realize now that telling the story and writing it to share with you has provided me with an amazing amount of healing. I no longer feel like these emotions and trauma are trapped inside of me and, infact, I believe the energy has been freed and transmuted.

I want to thank you for playing a role in my healing as this book was also written for you.

Love and Blessings,

Cynthia

Foreword by Dr. Sue Morter

There is an obvious and yet illusive living bridge between science and spirituality. It is called the human spirit, the soulful self. Within this vibrational space of the soul, we have access to all that has ever been and all that will ever be known. It is ours to investigate and explore how to master this place between the worlds and bring into harmony and alignment all facets of our consciousness so that we can ultimately experience our true nature - the oneness that is real.

When a soul enters into this life, every moment, every experience, every interaction is divinely designed as an opportunity for that soul to awaken, embody, and evolve. It is as if soulful contracts are being set in motion to support our evolution; agreements orchestrated at the very impetus of incarnation. That each connection and encounter be seen as supportive

– without exception - is our greatest challenge and yet holds our greatest opportunity for liberation.

Both cutting edge Quantum Science and ancient spirituality point us to perceive in this way. There is a divine pattern to all that is encountered, and we hold the key to manifest in accordance with limitless possibility. In my book '*The Energy Codes: The Seven Step System to Awaken the Spirit, Heal Your Body and Live Your Best Life*', I have referenced this as the "Bus Stop" Conversation. (While waiting to catch the bus to planet Earth we struck up conversations at the Bus Stop, determining how we might support each other in our great discovery of truth.) We create both challenging and celebratory moments to polish ourselves against one another in order to refine what we came to refine.

Oftentimes, this means that we encounter more than we thought we could manage. Yet, as divinity would have it, this is not possible. We are always a match for what unfolds. Accepting this renders us more awake and more capable than we possibly ever imagined – ultimately healing that which we thought was un-healable. As an awakening soul, we transform personal and ancestral trauma, discover the life-altering power of forgiveness, and ultimately, we realize the nature of the Self and all reality which is LOVE.

Cyndi Ambriz is one of these Souls.

In '*Life Finds a Way*', Cyndi honestly and artfully relays the story of her journey, but not as a victim of life's circumstances, despite how challenging and difficult they may be. Cyndi's story is one of an elevated view, the true interpretation of life events guiding the soul's awakening and journey of empowerment and love.

All of our stories are important; they are a record of our life's journey. How we choose to interpret and address those stories is *everything*.

As a doctor for more than thirty-five years and a spiritual and personal development teacher for more than twenty, I teach that everything in creation is energy, and that when we learn to work with the energy beneath the "story" — that raw energy and felt sensation rising within us in any situation — we are able to process that energy even more easily and gracefully than working with it on the level of the mind alone. We let the body help the mind do what it needs to do to prevail. When we do, we no longer stay stuck in resistance or denial of what has taken place in our life. Therefore, we are no longer "stuck" in our story, and our lives can move forward. When we get in touch with the energy beneath the story and know how to transmute and embody it, we are no longer trapped by the outer world and what has "happened to" us. We become both empowered and at peace, knowing that whatever takes place or appears in our life journey is there for the soul's ultimate awakening. Our only divine task is to look upon it from a place of love, just as Cyndi so masterfully illustrates with '*Life Finds a Way*'.

Whether it be challenges within the family from an early age, as Cyndi relays in her story, or an autoimmune diagnosis that creates limitations on your path, when we are able to see each and every experience as a gift of our awakening, our story and our life experience shifts tremendously.

The truth is, there is only one thing happening here, and it is in our favor. When we can truly embody this truth, as Cyndi has so skillfully shown in the telling of her own story of transformation, a new world opens to us.

We no longer feel separate or alone. Instead, we belong to our lives, and to every person we encounter. We see each as a fellow soul playing a character in our life story, one who has agreed to help us awaken in exactly the ways we need.

We no longer live disempowered or as a victim of our circumstances. Instead, we feel empowered, knowing that whatever is happening was meant for us and that we have everything we need within to transmute and not only survive but *thrive* from the situation. This is the energy of creation, the energy of which we were made. When we embody that energy, when we *know* it as truth, our experience (not what happens but how we see it and what we do within ourselves in the face of it), truly becomes our greatest creation.

The discovery of and embodiment of this truth and this way of being is a life-long process of learning. We came to this life to experience it *all*, and rather than labeling it *good* or *bad*, it is the interpretation of our experiences as unquestionably in our favor that is the real journey.

It is this devotion to our journey which ultimately serves our soulful evolution.

In '*Life Finds a Way*', one can see the transformative power of devotion in one's life. Cyndi's devotion to her path and learning has created not only her life story, but the woman she has become.

As a long-standing, active, and devoted member of Agape, her deep and sincere work with me and The Energy Codes®, and her openness and presence in seeking healing modalities and paths, she has demonstrated her unwavering dedication to spiritual growth. She has come into her own in a most beautiful way, and she can help you do the same.

It is her devotion that has allowed her to heal. The devotion to her path, to the interpretation and embodiment of her life circumstances, to herself, and to God, created a vibration of transformation within her. It is this heightened vibration which established an internal energetic environment, allowing her to rise above any limiting beliefs, stories, or feelings, and instead to remain in love, gratitude, and appreciation for all that life has delivered.

It is the devotion to healing and the spiritual journey of *'Life Finds a Way'* that allowed Cyndi to not only survive, but to thrive. It allowed her to step into being the ultimate creator of her life, rather than fall prey to the temptation to becoming a victim. It is the devotion that created the energetic vibrational match and embodiment of knowing that love *is* all there is. Accepting this energetic reality of allowing life to be a gift has allowed Cyndi to open to and become a greater truth for herself and others.

It is a joy to know and love and work alongside Cyndi in this world. I welcome you as well to this grand adventure of allowing life's gifts to be received. With Cyndi as your guide, you are in good hands.

With Great Love,

Dr. Sue Morter

Founder: Morter Institute for Bio-Energetics

Author: *The Energy Codes: The Seven Step System to Awaken Your Spirit, Heal Your Body and Live Your Best Life.*

Teacher: The Energy Codes Coursework

Introduction

"You came here to share your gifts." The first time I heard Rev. Michael Bernard Beckwith, founder of Agape International Spiritual Center in Los Angeles, say those words, I thought he was talking to everyone else in the sanctuary except me. It is not always easy to accept that we have a purpose, and that part of our purpose involves sharing our gifts. In my case, there were numerous things that prevented me from accepting his statement as my reality. To start, I wasn't brought up in an environment that affirmed this. In fact, the person I was when I first heard those words had been molded by my surroundings. I had believed that I needed to behave a certain way to be loved. This meant to do what others said, but not as they did. This meant not rocking the boat. This meant taking the abuse and then saying, "Yes" and "Thank you" after it all.

This meant that hearing about my innate gifts, and the subsequent spiritual development classes I took as a result, was all new for me.

The beautiful thing about Life is that it invites us – on a regular basis, through various experiences – to question the things we believe to be the truth about who we are and to challenge them. For example, I was a very outgoing child who conversed easily with people of all ages and backgrounds. By the time I was in my late thirties, I felt like a feral cat. I wanted to be invisible; I didn't want to be seen as I moved through life, let alone spoken to. It wasn't until I was in my mid-forties during my Practitioner Studies Program (more about this later) that I stood up to the belief that I was shy and terrified of public speaking. Life showed up with the perfect set of circumstances that enabled me to transcend that belief and the resulting behavior.

What if one of my innate gifts was my ability to share, connect, and interact with people unapologetically as demonstrated when I was a young child?

Although life circumstances had caused me to become shy, fearful, and apprehensive, this same life was beckoning me to my true self. The statement "Life is for me" – something that Rev. Michael says often – was beginning to make itself a permanent resident in my awareness.

How I viewed myself began to shift even more when I attended an Energy Codes workshop with Dr. Sue Morter, international speaker, Master of Bio-Energetic Medicine, and Quantum Field Visionary. During the workshop, Dr. Morter asked the audience, "How many of you had absent parents or deal with feelings of abandonment?" I slowly turned to scan the room and about 80 percent of the individuals had raised their hands. I felt safe to slowly lift mine. The next thing Dr. Sue said really grabbed and held my attention. "Big souls come in for big lessons and they usually get started right away. If you didn't have a father or a mother or both, it's because you are a very big soul who didn't need them," she said. After hearing her speak those words, I immediately thought, *Is it possible that all the suffering I have experienced in this life was not some unfortunate random set of events but something that was deliberate and purposeful? Am I one of the big souls she is referring to?*

Instantly, my entire life flashed before my eyes. Although my biological mother and father were not around much, I had always been blessed with the presence of incredibly wise people in my life. Spirit always brought people into my life who loved and encouraged me.

Dr. Sue also teaches a concept she calls "The Bus Stop Conversation." She describes it as the cosmic bus stop where we stand in line and wait for the bus that will bring us to Earth. While at the bus stop, souls strike up conversations and ask each other, "What are you going to Earth for?" A soul might say they are going to Earth for a level 10 experience in forgiveness, which would require someone to do something 'terrible' that that soul would need to forgive. This lifetime would require an entire cast of characters to play out the various roles, all with the assignment of helping that individual soul learn forgiveness. As the conversation continues, individual souls begin to sign up for the different roles that will help the soul accomplish its mission. Someone gets cast as the father who might be an abusive alcoholic. Another soul volunteers to play the role of the unloving mother, and so on, and so on. This book is a story about my level 10 bus stop conversation and how it has and continues to play out here on Earth.

Part of my bus stop involved experiencing Multi-Focal Motor Neuropathy – a medical condition where the immune system attacks the motor nerves. I would feel extreme weakness in my body and there were times when I'd lose mobility in my hands, arms, and legs. This condition has been part of the catalyst for my journey and quest to healing physically, mentally, emotionally, and spiritually.

I've been exploring the full spectrum of this human journey. I was the individual in our family who everyone turned to in his or her time of need, a pattern that repeated throughout much of my life. In and of itself, there was nothing wrong with being the person my family relied on; however, it became an issue when I began to neglect myself to serve them.

When the condition showed up, I was no longer able to tend to everyone else; it was time to tend to myself. Everything came up for me to reevaluate. I considered whether my marriage was something I could stay in while healing. I examined whether my workplace was conducive to healing. I had to look discriminately at all aspects of my life – from friendships to belief systems to long-standing ways of being. Everything needed to come up for review. Ultimately, I was and have been on a quest to discover what it means to be whole in mind, body, and spirit.

'Life Finds a Way' is an intimate look into my life. In these pages, I dive into some of my experiences along my healing journey, which lead to a deeper excavation and awareness of the unique gifts I am here to share. It is my hope that as you read my story, you'll be inspired to pause, reflect, and discern your life from and through the lens of purpose and intention. I hope you find comfort in knowing that everything does happen for a reason and that no matter how sweet or unsavory, it all serves our highest good. Lastly, my prayer is that you remember the vast power you have and are and that despite challenges, trauma, and circumstances, you can transform your life.

You have the power to live a life that is exciting, fulfilling, purposeful, and beneficial on every level. You just have to remember, trust, and allow it.

Chapter 1
My Family Lineage

One of my earliest memories is of my Aunt Hilda. Aunt Hilda was the youngest of my grandparents' 11 children. She was a beautiful soul and I believe she was an empath. Growing up in our family was not easy for her (or anyone else for that matter). Her mother, my maternal grandmother, Ernestina, died when Hilda was only 4 years old. Her oldest sister, Ana, was living abroad in the United States when she learned of her mother's passing. My Aunt Ana returned to Mexico for the funeral and from what I was told, she came with a vengeance. Ana blamed her father for her mother's death, even though the doctor who performed the autopsy listed the cause of death as a stroke.

My grandfather was born and raised in Louisiana and was of Creole descent. At some point, he decided to leave the U.S. and moved to Tampico, Mexico. I often wondered what caused him to leave his native country and family behind only to move to a country where he didn't speak the language. But a language barrier didn't deter him. Soon after his arrival, he purchased a ranch and started a dairy factory. Not long after, he met and married my grandmother. How my grandfather managed to court my grandmother without speaking her language is beyond me. I suppose she was captivated by his good looks and charm. I'm sure it helped that he was also an intelligent and successful businessman. My mother often said that my grandfather was a bit of an enigma. He was very secretive and rarely allowed anyone access or even a glimpse into his day-to-day life. According to my mother, he attended "secret" meetings and he wore – what she later discovered – a Freemason ring. She believed the Masons were a money-worshipping organization, but from what I have come to understand, the organization focuses on occult knowledge. No one really knew what my grandfather was involved in, yet almost everybody assumed and speculated that whatever he was up to was dark in nature.

My Aunt Ana was infuriated by her mother's death and was convinced that her father was to blame. She was set on revenge and wanted to hit her father where it would hurt him most: his children. Once back in Mexico, Ana spoke with her siblings one by one, sharing her theory that their father was at fault for their mother's death. She told her sisters and brothers that they would be in danger if they stayed with their father and told them they would be safe living with her. My Aunt Ana was so persuasive with her argument that she eventually had her siblings believing their lives would be endangered if they remained with their father. Without warning, Ana kidnapped Hilda, my mother, my aunt, and two of my uncles. Since my grandfather was American, the children had dual citizenship, so it was easy to get them out of the country.

Once in the U.S., the children were neglected and abused physically, mentally, and emotionally. Ana and her husband mistreated them terribly. I recall my mother telling me that during one of Ana's fits, she grabbed my mother by the hair and slammed her head into the doorknob, cracking her skull open. Hilda and my other aunt watched in horror and tried to stay out of the way; they didn't want to suffer the same fate. It wasn't long after that Ana decided to turn the children over to social services and each of them was placed in a different foster home.

My mom feels Hilda suffered the most as she was only 4 years old when her life unraveled. Not only did she find herself alone in a strange country without speaking the language but in a short amount of time she lost her mother, was separated from her father, and now was without her siblings.

Eventually, my grandfather was able to track his children down and made his way to Los Angeles. He showed up at a mechanic's shop in East Los Angeles where he heard my uncle was working. My uncle was 15 years old at the time and when he saw his father, he ran in the opposite direction. He still believed his father was a dangerous man based on what his sister had told him. This devastated my grandfather and he returned to Tampico a 'broken' man. My grandfather disappeared shortly after that, and it is speculated that two of his children may have been involved in his disappearance. The two oldest boys got their hands on their father's property and there was no one to contest. It's said that in the last days that my grandfather was seen, he would aimlessly wander the streets, carrying around his daughter's doll.

My mother did what she could to visit Hilda as often as possible over the years. I don't know what was worse – seeing Hilda or not going to see her. It was a tough and heartbreaking situation either way and saying goodbye to her baby sister only made things worse. My mother didn't want to leave Hilda, but she wasn't in the position to care for her just yet. To make things worse, it was becoming apparent that Hilda was experiencing bouts of depression as she was unresponsive during some of my mother's visits. Additionally, Hilda had developed a severe stutter and was teased and picked on by the other foster children because of it.

As time went on, each of the children turned of age and was released from the foster care system. Both my mom and aunt married shortly after leaving foster care and moved into a duplex in East Los Angeles. They lived next door to each other. Hilda was the last one to age out. Once Hilda turned 18, she moved in with her sisters, splitting her time between the two homes.

I was born shortly after Hilda moved in. Hilda took an instant liking to me, and she treated me as if I was her own. She helped my mom take care of me and spent much of her time playing with me. Hilda would go back and forth between our home and my aunt's. It was not difficult to spot the dysfunction in both homes. My mother and father fought frequently, and one time their fighting was so bad that my mother miscarried. Despite the tense and mercurial environment, things seemed to be OK with my Aunt Hilda, at least on the surface.

One day, Hilda convinced my mom, dad, aunt and uncle to go out for the afternoon. She insisted they take the kids as she needed some alone time. When we returned from our outing, we walked into the house to find the record player playing Hilda's favorite song. As my mother walked into the bedroom, she discovered Hilda's body on the floor. My beautiful aunt had taken her leave by shooting herself in the chest with my uncle's shotgun. I know it seems impossible for me to remember as I was only one year old, but I do.

My mother was never the same after Hilda's death. All that survival and struggle they endured, and for what? Only for the youngest to end up dead.

Several of my mother's siblings died at young ages and for this reason, I always thought that I, too, would die young. It seemed to be the fate that awaited me.

Aunt Hilda's death seemed to foreshadow the many transitions up ahead for my family, and it wasn't long before my parents' relationship unraveled as well. By the time I was 5 years old – four years after Aunt Hilda's passing – my parents divorced, and I was devastated. I loved both of my parents, but I was devastated when my dad left. He was a buffer between me and my mom; he was my safety net from my mom's frequent beatings and now he was gone.

After the divorce, my dad would pick me up on the weekends. One day, he pulled up in a black Mustang, handed me a pair of sunglasses, and said, "Today we are movie stars." He then drove us to Santa Monica beach for the day. My father was a wild soul who never outgrew his adolescence. How could he? It's not like the men in our culture were encouraged to seek counseling to help them process their emotions and trauma.

I suppose the same can be applied to my mother. She was all about working hard so that we could have a place to live, clothes on our backs, and food on the table but she didn't know the first thing about providing a nurturing and healthy environment for her children. In fact, I suspect the way she treated me stemmed from the example set by her parents and later by her older sister, Ana.

It's often said that our parents do as much as they can and then they pass on the baton to the next person. It's not hard to figure out what our mission will be. All I needed to do was look at what my parents struggled with. On some level prior to incarnating, I must have agreed to pick up that baton and see how far I could go with it before it was time to pass it on to the next generation. I am the one my ancestors prayed for, and it was time to break those cycles that had plagued my family for generations. It was time to heal seven generations forward and seven generations back.

Chapter 2
Near Calls and Near Misses

There was a recurring theme that played throughout most of my life: Near calls. And by this, I mean a consistent pattern of me coming close to death and dying. The first near-death experience happened when I was still a toddler and learning how to crawl. I loved being in the kitchen – it was a place that I enjoyed playing in. I played in the kitchen often and would head straight to the cabinet where the shiny pots and pans waited for me. There was something fascinating about pots, lids and food storage boxes. Maybe it was the way they stacked together. Maybe it was the *clink-clank* sound they made when I pushed them into each other. One thing is certain, I was enamored.

One day, my mom put me down on the living room floor with my bottle while she jumped in the shower. Once I finished my bottle, I decided to play in the kitchen. I crawled past the cabinet with the pots and pans and went to the cabinet beneath the kitchen sink. I didn't have access to that cabinet because there was normally an adult standing there washing dishes, blocking access to the cabinet. But not that day. I opened the cabinet and instead of seeing those shiny pots, I discovered a huge bag filled with pebble-looking things. Being the curious child that I was, I opened the bag, grabbed a handful of the pebbles, and placed them in my mouth. Those 'pebbles' turned out to be rat pellets, which were 100 percent toxic. I began to convulse and foam at the mouth almost immediately. Soon after, I felt light and observed my body as I floated near the ceiling. I remember darting back and forth between the kitchen and the bathroom trying to get my mom's attention. As I hovered above my body, I noticed it was turning purple. Eventually, my mom came into the kitchen and found me sprawled out on the floor. She rushed me to the hospital to have my stomach pumped.

I have said this often throughout my life, "Despite my parents' inadequacies, I would never wish me on anyone." The pebble incident wouldn't be the first time I would tempt death. I wondered if all my 'accidents' were my attempt at trying to leave this physical realm due to the difficulty of what was ahead.

∽

Near Misses and Seizures

Staying alive was not going to be the easiest thing for me to do. A few months after the rat pellet incident, I was riding in the front seat of our car with my mother and father. Before anyone could process what was happening, my father crashed into the car in front of us, which sent me flying out of my mother's lap towards the steering wheel. One of the keys on the key ring pierced through my skull, sending both of my parents into a state of shock and panic. The paramedics arrived and rushed me to the hospital. Once there, the doctors informed my parents that the key had missed my brain by a fraction of an inch. I still bear the scar just above my right brow.

As if the random accidents weren't enough, I suffered from bouts of seizures, which I had experienced since birth. Seizures had become a part of my life and I eventually developed an automatic response to them. Each time a seizure came on, my mother would rush me to the emergency room where I was placed in an ice bath to tamper my high fever. (Those ice baths were uncomfortable!) We visited the ER so much that I remember being in the hospital lobby with no apparent supervision, watching as the foot traffic went by for hours on end. I remember in those moments wishing and thinking to myself that I didn't need to be there and desperately wanting to go home.

At a certain point, I was able to sense when a seizure was coming, and I preferred dealing with it at home instead of the ER. As soon as I felt the seizure coming on, I'd run towards the bathroom while undressing, yelling for Mom to start bringing the ice in. My mom and I had our seizure protocol and procedure which served us just fine, that is until the day it interfered with something I really wanted to do.

I started preschool when I was 4 years old and I remember being so excited to start venturing out into the big world outside of my home, without my parents. On this one day, I was excited about going to school because there was a field trip to the zoo planned, and I had never been to the zoo before. As I was getting dressed, my mother told me I wasn't going to school that day. "You can't go on the field trip because of the seizures," she said. I felt a sudden wave of dread wash over me. I straightened my back, stood a little taller, and peered intently and seriously into my mom's eyes. In that moment I decided and informed my mother I would never have another seizure again as long as I lived. Something in my eyes or stance must have convinced my mother because she reluctantly drove me to school. As we walked into the classroom, my mom asked me to repeat to my teacher what I had told her earlier while at home. I looked up at my teacher and explained to her that she had nothing to worry about because I would no longer have any more seizures. Before I knew it, I was sitting on the bus, on my way to the zoo.

That day I walked around the zoo and looked in curiosity and wonder at the giraffes, zebra, monkeys, and other animals for the first time. I was in deep amazement. At the end of our visit, we ate our lunch at a nearby park. After drinking my last bit of juice to wash down my sandwich, I climbed up the ladder to the top of the slide. As I came down, I raised both arms in a position of victory.

That was the first moment in my life where I healed something in an instant. The only thought worth entertaining in that moment was going to the zoo and nothing else. And because I was so set on going to the zoo, my belief and full faith that I would go was all the determination and will I needed to heal myself of seizures. I haven't experienced a seizure since.

Chapter 3
Staying Alive

I grew up in a home where physical, verbal, and emotional abuse were constant companions. It was a rare occasion when I wasn't being hit or yelled at or witnessing someone else in my family experience abuse. The abuse was so present in my family's fabric that I came to believe that it was normal and the way it was supposed to be.

When I wasn't getting hit or yelled at, I would lose myself in a world of fantasies – in my imagination. In my imagination, everything was available to me. On some days, I was a botanist. I would explore the various plants in our garden and would pluck a few of them as samples to see what they tasted like and to determine their medicinal purposes. My curiosity upset our landlady, who would yell and complain anytime she caught me in the garden plucking away.

At other times, I was an architect and specialized in building houses out of blankets in our living room. And then there were times when I imagined that I was a Kung Fu Master, second only to Bruce Lee. There was nothing I could not be or do as a child – at least not in my imagination.

One of my favorite past times was playing with my mother's LP collection and dancing in our living room. Our living room was your typical 70s setup – complete with a red shag carpet and a green glass ball lamp. Anytime I got the chance to play my favorite songs, I would. During a rare moment of peace in our house, my father and grandmother sat in the living room and watched as I danced to my heart's delight. I danced until I had emptied my lungs of all air. I danced until the energy in my body had seeped out, leaving me exhausted yet exhilarated. I danced as if it was my last dance. My father and grandmother were so entertained.

When I was 5 years old, my cousins took me to see my first movie in a theater, *Saturday Night Fever*. After they saw how much I enjoyed it, they gave me the 8-track of the movie's soundtrack. I adored John Travolta. I wanted to be John Travolta. My cousins and I would choreograph dance routines set to disco music and hosted our own showcases. We even recruited some of the neighborhood kids. I may have been young, but it was obvious that I was in my element.

I was bitten by the disco bug and its effects were pulsating in my blood. I couldn't get enough of it, and it was the one thing I preferred to do all the time.

One day during my kindergarten year, I was standing alone on the playground, deep in thought and wishing I was home dancing. As I began to look around at the distant pockets of children, I noticed the playground gate was open. I walked towards the gate and continued to walk through it since no one stopped me. I kept walking until I got home. Once home, I didn't know how I was going to get inside, so I stopped by the landlady's unit and asked to borrow her key. I let myself in, put on the 8-track to *Saturday Night Fever*, and went off into disco Neverland. Midway through "I'm, I'm, I'm, I'm staying alive, staying alive," I turned towards the front door and saw my mother standing there, her eyes burning with a fury that my body would soon feel. My first thought was to make a dash for the back door, but I didn't think I would make it. My next thought was to simply wave the white flag and pay the piper – and boy was the piper upset. My mom lunged at me and beat me with every ounce of strength and force that she could muster. She flung me by the hair in every direction and tossed me around like a rag doll.

Although the pain was a lot to bear, those brief moments of freedom had been worth it. For a moment, I had been John Travolta dancing to the Bee

Gees. *I'm, I'm, I'm, I'm staying alive, staying alive.* I had no idea at the time how this song would become my theme song on my journey.

Chapter 4
Darkness Descends

F rom my vantage, it didn't seem that my mom gave much thought to selecting spouses. I had heard my mother complain for years about the types of men she attracted. She emphasized how worthless and terrible of a person my father was and her complaining and criticizing only increased as time went on. Even as a child I wondered what inspired my mom to marry these men if she knew she didn't like them to begin with. It was hard for me to comprehend and was above what I could make sense of at the time.

I was about 9 years old when my mother remarried. The whole marriage was strange to me for many reasons. To start, I didn't see this man around much before they announced their plans to wed.

Where had he come from? Who was he?

I didn't trust him. To top it off, I was sent to stay with an aunt the week they got married, although my younger brother was allowed to stay.

From the outside looking in, it appeared that my family was moving on up. We had relocated from East Los Angeles to a three-bedroom house in Huntington Park, a suburb of Los Angeles County. My stepfather worked the swing shift at a nearby factory and worked evenings as a master of ceremonies at the local nightclubs. He spent much of his time away from home and didn't return until the early hours of the morning. At some point early during their marriage, my mom and stepfather stopped sleeping in the same bed, and my stepfather moved into the spare bedroom.

I was addicted to television and often would fall asleep in front of it while watching a favorite movie or show. When my stepfather came in for the night from work, he would pick me up and carry me up to my bed. This had become common, and I didn't think anything of it. One night while lying asleep on the couch with the TV playing, I awoke to him kissing me. I was shocked and didn't know what to do or what to say. So, I said nothing at all and feigned sleep. I was frozen in place and couldn't wait for it to be over. Sadly, things only worsened from that point forward. Although I tried not to fall asleep in the living room anymore, I loved watching TV too much.

And what started out as him kissing me turned into him placing his hands down my underwear and inappropriately touching me. After so many times of this, I stopped falling asleep in the living room and would go to my bedroom as soon as I felt myself getting sleepy. I started sleeping with a knife under my pillow after that.

A few months had passed since those moments with my stepfather when he and my mom decided to have a gathering over at our house. I was cleaning in preparation for our guests, dusting and tidying up my parents' bedroom, when I noticed that the jewelry box was out of place. I moved it back to where it belonged and discovered a white powdery substance underneath. Not thinking anything of it, I brushed it onto the floor. My stepfather came into the room right as I was finishing up dusting and began to question me incessantly about what was beneath the jewelry box. I shrugged my shoulders and explained to him that whatever it was, I had wiped it onto the floor. My mom walked in right as I was telling him what happened. Unknown to me at the time, that moment was my introduction to drugs.

A few weeks after the powdery substance incident, my stepfather told my mother that he was leaving her for another woman. My mom was enraged and as revenge, she took a big rock from outside and smashed his state-of-the-art television set. In return, my stepfather picked up a large rock of his own and shattered the living room window, which was the size of the entire wall. My mom, who was overcome with anger, took a knife and ripped up all his fancy suits that my stepfather would emcee in. My stepfather left that day and although I felt for my mother and the pain she was feeling, I can't say that I was sad to see him go.

Overcome with raging passion and grief, my mom began consulting a witch named Grace. Grace reminded me of Stygian witches from the movie *Clash of the Titans*. I wasn't sure if my mom hired Grace to help her get my stepfather back or to cause him harm, or both. For some reason, my mom decided to take me with her to one of her sessions at Grace's house. When we arrived, Grace, an older woman, asked mom if she had gotten her what she asked for and my ears perked up. Mom went to the trunk of the car and pulled out two live roosters, one red and one black. My eyes widened to the size of saucers at what I saw next. I watched as Grace wrung and cut off the necks of both roosters. The blood was to be used in some sort of ritual bath. I remember watching in disbelief as the witch covered my mother in a red substance. As they finished up, Grace handed my mom a powder to scatter in front of the mistress's home.

Immediately after we left the witch's home, mom headed over to the other woman's house. She jumped out of the car and poured the contents on the woman's front yard, but not before the mistress's mother spotted us. Some hours later, I noticed the same woman standing in front of our home, scattering a powder of her own. It turned out that the mistress and her mom were no strangers to witchcraft. These women were in an energetic battle over my stepfather, and I couldn't understand why. When I went into the hallway closet for something some days later, I knew something was about to go terribly wrong. On the top shelf stood a black, Devil-shaped candle, with a pitchfork atop a wax mountain. The candle had several pins inserted into it. I never asked mom about it or shared what I saw with anyone.

I later learned that when an individual works with black magic, it comes back to that person three-fold. Since my mom used black magic to harm her 'enemies' it came back around, but not just to my mom – it affected all of us. Within a few months, I was hit by our own car, my brother was hit by a car in front of my eyes, and my sister swallowed a jar full of my mother's Valium. All of this occurred back-to-back within a span of three months.

Years later while visiting an aunt, she shared with me that mom had told her about the various spells she had cast on my stepfather. My aunt proceeded to tell me that it was up to me to break the curses that afflicted my family. To do so, I would need to go to the house we lived in when I was 12 and dig up the spell bundles my mother buried in the backyard. My aunt said this was the only way to release us from all the misfortune. I never did.

Ultimately, I took another route, but I always remembered what she said to me about the dangers of working with black magic.

Chapter 5
The Accident

S ummer vacation had begun, and I was too excited for the sunny days out with friends without homework and early rises. I had just finished my sixth-grade school year (1983) and as a treat, my mom was taking us out. Fun was something we didn't focus on or experience often in our family, so when my mom shared her plans with us, I was thrilled. On the first official day of summer break, I woke up early to thoughtfully pick out what I was going to wear. As a rule, we had to look our best when going out with mom.

I created my outfit from the ground up because my new pair of tennis shoes – white with a baby blue swoosh emblem on the side – were to be the focus. If it was possible to love shoes, then I loved them. I then chose a cute, white skirt and a pink knit sweater. I gave myself a glance over and liked what I saw.

Everything was coming together nicely and as I envisioned. As I finished brushing my hair, I heard mom frantically yelling, "My daughter, my daughter!" I ran out of my bedroom as fast as I could and proceeded to run out the kitchen door, which led to our driveway. I stood for a second trying to figure out what was happening as my mom screamed hysterically. I followed my mom's gaze and noticed our car, moving in reverse and out of our driveway.

If mom is standing there, who is driving the car?

The car crossed the street and went into the front neighbor's yard. It drove so straight that you would have thought someone was behind the wheel.

People began coming out of their houses, partially because of my mother's incessant screaming and to see what was going on. I think we all thought and hoped the car would come to a stop after crashing into the neighbor's brick fence. Instead, the car shifted back into drive and then began moving again – this time in a forward motion. As I watched in disbelief, the car drove itself across the street and headed back into our driveway. Mom ran to the car and tried to open the driver's side door. That's when I realized my 2-year-old sister was in the car. Time slowed down and everything moved in an exaggerated slow motion. And in that moment, I thought, *can I stop it?*

My 12-year-old body was no competition for that boat of a car, but I stood in front of it anyway. The initial impact knocked the wind right out of me as I was sucked underneath the car by what felt like some unseen vacuum. My mother ran towards the car, expecting to see me laying on the floor, but the car kept going, dragging me along with it. Our driveway was long and as the car drove past the side of the house, I felt a huge snap, which might have been my knee as it slammed against the corner of the house. The car kept going until it crashed through the garage wall, eventually lodging itself and finally coming to a stop.

My mom, who was in total hysteria, climbed onto the trunk of the car to access the interior and turn the car off. She was afraid my sister would shift the car into gear, and it would begin moving again. The problem was when mom jumped on the trunk of the car, the car lowered, and the muffler came down and burned my left calf. The muffler burned straight through to the bone. I let out a loud, piercing scream, and mom jumped off the car.

"My daughters are dead, my daughters are dead," she screamed. I responded,

"We are not dead, call an ambulance!" Thankfully, one of the neighbors called 911.

While my sister was trapped in the car, I was pinned beneath it, shaped like a pretzel. Both of my feet were in the vicinity of my head. My right foot hung over my left shoulder while my left foot was in my mouth.

As I bit down on my foot, the only thing I could think about was my new shoes.

As time passed, it became harder and harder to breathe. I could feel the weight of the car as it pressed down on my lungs. And then the unexpected happened. Silence hovered as everything around me became still. I had entered a peaceful state, one in which I was very aware of my thoughts. I was floating in and out of consciousness. Although young, I had developed a strong sense of independence and seldom asked for help. In that moment, it occurred to me that that moment was a good time to ask for help.

Who exactly was I to reach out to, though?

I began attending catechism classes when I was 7 years old. Most people complete the program within two years. I was 12 and had not successfully completed catechism. I was unmotivated and it may have been because I didn't believe what the nuns were saying. I also had a hard time memorizing and reciting prayers. On most Sundays, instead of attending class, I would go into the Big D grocery store on the corner, purchase a box of popsicles and eat them until catechism class let out. Then, I would return home. My only concern was that I hoped no one noticed my red lips from eating all those popsicles. Week after week this had been my routine. Since no one ever asked me about class, I never said.

In that moment when I asked for help while pinned down under our family car, all the prayers I had not been able to memorize during the previous five years came flowing out of my mouth.

"Our Father who art in Heaven, hallowed be Thy name. Thy Kingdom come, Thy will be done, on Earth as it is in Heaven... "

I said those prayers fervently and loudly as I gazed out onto the driveway.

"Hail Mary full of grace the Lord is with me." I was surprised to realize the prayers had been inside of me all along. In that moment, I felt the car lift and a stream of air rushed into my lungs. No one was near the car, so I suspect God and/or the angels had intervened.

It took the firemen a while to figure out how they could gain access to me without hurting me any further as the car was lodged in the garage wall. Eventually, I heard them breaking down the wall with sledgehammers. Once the wall was down, they used a jack to lift the car, and out I slid. A firefighter was the first person I saw, and I was elated to see him. He took me in his arms like the damsel in distress that I was and began to ask me my name, date of birth, and my age to see how lucid and conscious I was. I answered him but a deep sleep was coming over me. I don't know if it was my imagination, but I believe he slapped me to wake me up. He then proceeded to ask the same questions again.

I must have lost consciousness shortly after that line of questioning. The last thing I remembered was being placed in the ambulance and when I came to, I was in a white room with a bright white light.

Now you went and did it. You must be dead, and this must be Heaven! I thought.

Just then, I felt a terrible pain coming from my vaginal area.

What's that all about?

I used my one working limb and yanked at whatever was causing me discomfort. (I later found out it was a catheter.)

Why on Earth would anyone put that in me?

I began to feel blood dripping onto the floor, which caught the nurse's attention. "What did you do?" she asked, rushing over to check my vitals and inspect my handiwork. I looked at her and realized that since I was able to see her and she was talking to me, then I must not have been dead. What a relief.

I was wheeled into the emergency room and mom was there waiting, along with what looked like a sea of doctors, nurses, and technicians. The firemen who rescued me all stood at the foot of the gurney. As they handed me over to the hospital team, I couldn't help but sense their concern.

How bad could it be?

I asked my mom for a mirror. I wanted to see what I looked like as I had been dragged quite a distance along the pavement. My aunt had always referred to me as "my beautiful" and I had a feeling she wouldn't be calling me that anymore. No one I asked handed me a mirror.

Everyone worked diligently over a course of several hours to get me stabilized to assess the extent of the injuries. Later that evening, I was taken to a room on a higher floor which would be my home for the next three months. I could hear the doctors telling my mother they would have to wait for the swelling to go down before they could perform any kind of surgery and luckily for me, they had determined there was no internal bleeding. My dad arrived just around this time and when he saw me, he broke down. I don't think I had ever seen my dad cry before so I figured I must have looked bad for him to break down like that.

I didn't have much alone time but once I did, I used my one working arm to lift the bedsheet. What I saw no longer looked like human legs but more like an elephant's legs – they were huge! I could not believe how swollen my legs were. It took about three weeks for the swelling to go down enough for the doctors to begin what would be a series of operations. The first surgery involved:

1. Left knee surgery where the doctors put in a set of pins as the knee had been shattered.
2. Left hip surgery - A pin was placed in my left hip as it was broken in three places.
3. Skin graft – Skin was taken from my inner left thigh area and placed over the muffler burn on my left calf.
4. The right hip and left shoulder were dislocated so they attached a set of weights to the right leg to keep it straight and my left arm was placed in a sling.

I woke up after the initial surgery screaming as the pain was excruciating and unbearable. I had been in surgery for eight hours.

The next day the doctors stopped by to update us on the surgery and how things went. Dr. Weight, my internist, was happy to report there was no internal damage and that the skin graft had gone well. Dr. Bowen, the orthopedic surgeon, was happy overall with the surgeries and shared that the growth plate in my left knee was severely damaged. He explained that the growth plate supports 70 percent of the human body's growth. Since my left leg would not grow anymore, he would have to stop the growth in the right leg in the coming weeks. I was only 12 years old, and the height that I was at that time was as tall as I was going to be.

The whole experience was intense, and it required several more surgeries. I could not have been more thankful for western medicine and my two amazing doctors. My gratitude was tested, however, when I overheard the doctors tell my mother that it was likely I wouldn't walk again.

"These doctors have no idea who I am" I thought through a pain injection haze, before I drifted off into a deep sleep.

I was given heroin injections once every three hours to help manage the intense pain I felt. After noticing me shift from excruciating pain to falling sound asleep after the injection, my mother inquired into the ingredients of the shots. My doctors informed her it was a form of heroin and she lost it.

"I can't take her home as a junkie!" she yelled.

They explained the shots were necessary and that they knew how to wean people off before they left the hospital. They assured her all would be well. Over time, it became harder for me to make it through the three-hour periods without screaming for someone to administer the next shot. I was in intolerable pain, and I was aware that my body had become dependent on the drugs.

Earlier I mentioned that I hadn't completed catechism, and this is where it gets a little ironic: The hospital I was taken to after the accident was St. Francis Hospital in Lynwood, California. I had no idea religious hospitals existed, let alone ones where nuns visited patients. One day, as I laid in bed, a nun popped into my room and introduced herself.

"Hello, my name is Sister Cynthia," she said and invited herself in.

She asked if I made my first communion and I responded that I had not. She quickly assigned herself to me and informed me that we would begin catechism lessons the following day. I found it interesting that despite my lack of interest in catechism, there seemed to be no way of escaping it. Sister Cynthia showed up the next day as promised, and my daily lessons began. Surprisingly, I enjoyed her and the lessons. Over the coming weeks, I memorized the prayers and eventually made my first communion from my hospital bed.

After a couple more surgeries, I was discharged from the hospital. I wasn't walking yet but I knew that it was only a matter of time. I was determined to prove the doctor wrong. After a few days of being back home, I created my own 'learning to walk again' regimen. I waited for mom to go out and then I would get myself out of the wheelchair. I felt like I was starting all over again, and, in many ways, I was. I had to get used to my body, as so much had changed. I crawled around the floor on hands and knees and would scoot slowly to get a feel for moving. Eventually, I found the strength to stand and would take small steps, wobbly, but still steps. One day my mom returned early from her errands, and I was too far from the wheelchair to get back in. My mom caught me standing in the middle of the dining room.

"What do you think you're doing?" she asked.

"Walking," I responded. I don't know if she was proud of me, infuriated at me, or both.

Every couple of weeks, my mom and I visited the orthopedic surgeon for follow-ups. This was the same doctor who told my mom I wouldn't walk again. The look on his face when I walked into his office for my first follow-up appointment was priceless. That day, I traded in my wheelchair for a pair of crutches. Before we left, the doctor emphasized to my mom and me that because of the high amounts of heroin I was given, there was an 80 percent chance that I'd become addicted to drugs if I ever tried them.

Drugs and developing an addiction to them were the least of my concerns at that time. My summer vacation was nearing an end and I had spent practically the whole time in the hospital. Despite not having much of a summer break, I was ready to start the year with everyone else. Luckily, my mom agreed to let me go back to school. Since I still used and depended on my crutches, my 7-year-old brother and I walked to and from school together. When we arrived home from our first day at school, the skin beneath my armpits burned. I had walked to and from school, about 10 city blocks in each direction, on crutches and the skin in that area had peeled off. I didn't mention this to anyone. The next day, I asked my brother to stand close to me and instead of using my crutches, I held onto his shoulder. This was how we walked to and from school and it became our daily routine for about three months. In the mornings, I dressed myself then waited for him at the front door where he offered his shoulder and off to school, we went. Thank God children don't listen to or believe everything they are told and that the will of my 12-year-old self knew better. The only reality I allowed myself to hold in my mind was one where I played outside with my friends and did all the things a 12-year-old girl did.

I am amazed at the body's ability to heal and the intelligence that it possesses. What I was not aware of at the time, however, was the other aspects of healing I would need to address later. I wasn't aware that I would need to heal the energetic imprint from that traumatic experience. Many years later in 2016, I scheduled a healing session with a visiting Shaman from Peru named Wachan Bajiyoperak. I met Wachan and his family years earlier at a New Year's meditation retreat and felt called to work with him. As he began the ceremony, he said,

"The soul knows when the body is about to die, and your soul popped out of the body the day of the accident."

The funny thing about that comment was that I used to have a recurring dream where I saw myself sitting on the roof of my car, trying to drive the car from the roof as it sped backwards through the streets of downtown Los Angeles. I think my soul was trying to navigate or drive the vehicle (my body) while hovering somewhere above my head.

I know something in the invisible realm intervened on the day of the accident. I had asked for help through prayer or, as my minister Rev. Michael says, "H.E.L.P – Hello Eternal Loving Presence." Was that accident my way of saying,

"Hello, God. It's time. I am ready?"

It was not my time to leave the planet yet. There was more for me to experience, heal, and share.

Chapter 6
Drugs and the Law

My mom went from my stepfather who 'dabbled' in drugs and pedophilia to associating with the local Mexican Mafia. She was involved romantically and professionally with these individuals and went from being a naïve housewife to a drug dealer.

I was 14 years old when mom moved us from West Covina, a suburban neighborhood, to the drug-and-gang-infested neighborhood of Cudahy. One morning as I went to sit on the couch, I noticed the cushion was not laying right. I lifted it to see what was underneath and saw a rifle hidden there. It belonged to whoever was currently in my mom's bedroom. I knocked on her door and was shushed away.

Who had my mother become? Who were these people she kept bringing into our home?

When the man emerged from my mom's room, I immediately felt disgusted at his appearance. He looked like Homer Simpson's boss, Monty Burns.

What was my mother doing with him?

She was way too beautiful for him. Later that night, I found out what they were doing; it seems this man had left my mother in charge of a couple of kilos of cocaine.

Since we lived in a ghetto neighborhood, it wasn't uncommon to hear police sirens and helicopters throughout the day and night. One evening, my mom awoke to a helicopter flying over our apartment building, with the floodlight cascading over our entire house. My mom woke me up and nervously asked me to help her. She went and sat by the toilet with a couple of bricks of cocaine. She asked me what I thought she should do with it and I told her she needed to get rid of the evidence. Immediately, we began breaking up the packages and flushed them down the toilet as quickly as we could. Before long, the helicopter was gone. The police never came to the door. Unfortunately for my mother, she had to face the owner of the drugs the next day and explain to him what happened. (I was so happy when she returned home the next day because it meant she was alive!)

The following week, a different man was at our home, and I was shocked that my mom was continuing with these dealings. I felt that I needed to do something drastic to snap some sense into her. I knocked on her bedroom door and didn't get a response. I decided to run away from home. I called my friend Tina and asked her to come to get me. I placed my brother and sister in the bathtub so they wouldn't see me leave.

Tina took me to her home in Culver City where she lived with her mother. Tina was 18 years old, and I was 15. I was one of the youngest in our circle of friends. That night we went dancing at Don Quixote (DQs for short) in East L.A., one of the hot spots at that time. I got up to go to the bathroom, and as I looked in the mirror, saw my mother walking toward me. She grabbed me by the hair, dragged me outside, and kicked me repeatedly while I laid on the ground. I tried to shield myself and yelled out,

"I don't want to live with you anymore!" She stopped kicking me and left. I got up as quickly as I could and headed back into the club before she changed her mind and came back. I cleaned myself up and returned to our table.

I remained away from home for 28 days. I spent much of that time dancing the nights away, meeting new people, and staying with different friends. I was fortunate nothing 'bad' happened to me during this time. All I can attribute it to is God and my guardian angels. Periodically, I called home to speak to my brother and sister without my mother knowing. At a certain point, I realized my plan to shock her straight had not worked and it was time to go home. When I arrived home, my uncle was waiting for me. I was to go with him to Brownsville, Texas. Mom didn't want me around. She said the time in Texas would keep me away from negative friends, but I felt it was more personal than that.

I found it interesting that my mom was sending me with this particular uncle as he was my favorite. He had four daughters and when I was growing up, I always wanted to stay with them, but mom wouldn't let me. One time, I convinced her to let me spend the night at their house. She showed up in the middle of the night and dragged me out of the bed by my hair.

"Why do you think it's OK to treat Cynthia this way?" my uncle asked. He did his best to intervene, but my mother wasn't listening. As she drove, she managed to beat me all the way home, hitting me on my face, arms, and legs. The entire time, I wondered why.

Why was my mother beating me? Why was her response to everything to hit me?

I never understood why she didn't love me when she was my everything.

Chapter 7
On the Run

My mother had purchased a new home in the city of South Gate, a neighboring city of Cudahy, while I was away in Texas. When I returned a few months later, I realized that although the address had changed, nothing else did. In fact, things seemed to worsen. There were even more people coming in and out of our home.

One day, mom asked me if I would deliver a package to her friend who lived nearby. I told her I would and when I got in the car, I decided to open the small package to see what it was. It was the same white substance I had seen when I was 9 years old underneath the jewelry box in my parents' room. I touched it with my index finger and placed it on my tongue. To my surprise, it numbed my tongue. I had a feeling that it might help me to eat less as I had become a chubby teenager. When I returned home later that day, I found where my mother hid the other packets and I snuck one out. I figured she wouldn't miss it. I lost about 30 pounds in two months. Some of my mom's friends commented on my weight loss but no one took the time to really inquire.

The rest of that year went by quickly and before I knew it, we were in the holiday season. That Christmas was the first time that it was only me and my mother in the house by ourselves. My mom sat at the dining room table, with her cigarette in one hand and her drink in the other. For once, we were having a civil conversation. It had been a while since she and I bonded, and it felt good to have that time with her minus the fights, beatings, and arguments.

"Do you smoke?" my mom asked to my surprise. I looked at her and sheepishly confessed that I did.

"If you are going to smoke, I don't want you taking cigarettes from strangers," she said.

"So, you will get them from me."

Oh, she does care, I thought.

I asked her to excuse me for a moment as I needed to get something from my room. I must have been taking too long because my mom came to see what I was doing. My mom walked into my room, which startled me; I dropped the packet containing the cocaine. She bent over, picked it up, and said,

"Oh… so you're doing drugs now are you?" Then she continued,

"Well, if you are going to do them, you might as well do them with me," and she led me back to the dining room table.

That was the only time my mom and I did drugs together, and to be honest, I was startled and irritated by the whole thing. The reason why I even started doing drugs, to begin with, was to get my mother's attention. I hoped that if she saw her daughter doing drugs that she'd have a change of heart and would stop putting herself and our family in danger. Sadly, that didn't happen.

A few weeks after that night with Mom, I received a call from the San Diego Federal Jail. My mother had been arrested. She went to Tijuana the day before to see the dentist. While at the border, the agent suspected something was off and sent her into the secondary inspection area. My mom had decided to drive her boyfriend's car instead of her own and as it turned out, the car's tires were loaded with cash and drugs. This was a federal offense as she was crossing an international border with drugs.

My mother spent the night in jail and then went before a judge the following morning. She explained to the judge that she had three minor children waiting for her at home. He gave my mom a break and allowed her to leave on bail, then set her court date for a month later. I don't know who gets released on bail when such large amounts of drugs are confiscated but I guess she had an angel looking after her as well.

When mom came home, I assumed everything was going to change for the better. I assumed that she would sever her relationship with these people and do what was necessary to get herself out of that ordeal. Unfortunately, this was not to be the case. Instead, she stayed at her boyfriends' house, and my siblings and I didn't see much of her that month. I'm sure the boyfriend and his brother were nervous and wanted to keep a close eye on her to ensure that she wouldn't talk to the police. The day before mom was to return to San Diego for her court appearance, she fled the country. Before leaving, she found a random family to stay with my siblings and me in our house.

"They will take care of you and your siblings," she said.

I couldn't believe what was happening. That family was probably in need of a place to stay and had no idea what they had gotten themselves into.

The day after my mom was to appear in court, two federal agents arrived at our home looking for her. I told them that my mom had left the country and that I thought I could talk her into coming back so they wouldn't turn us over to social services. They agreed to give me some time.

Since I oversaw the house, they set certain parameters within which to function. I could use my mom's car to drive the kids to school and run errands, such as grocery shopping and paying bills. As an aside, I was 15 years old and didn't even have a driver's license. But that's how things played out; I had to grow up fast.

We were under 24-hour surveillance. Each time mom called, the agents listened. Some days they stood next to me in the kitchen and would tell me what to say or ask of her. Eventually, she spoke with them directly. The good thing about being under 24-hour surveillance was that the 'bad guys' couldn't get to us. I got to know the agents well but my familiarity with them wouldn't stop what was to come.

After a few months, the agents shared that they had given my mom more than enough time to turn herself in. They advised us that we should prepare for social services to come and retrieve us the next day. I was disappointed in my mother. I couldn't believe she was allowing this to happen. I couldn't believe she would be OK with her children being given to social services like she and her siblings were. I was devastated that she couldn't muster up the courage to turn herself in and save us.

We were officially out of time.

Chapter 8
The Savior

After the agents left for the day, my friend Libby and I came up with a plan. Libby asked an acquaintance if he would give us a ride that night to the bus station. She asked him to park the car in the alley behind our house after dark so that the federal agents who were parked out front would not see us leaving. In the middle of the night, we snuck my brother and sister out the back door, jumped the brick wall, and got into the getaway car. Our hearts raced as we drove to the bus station. Luckily, no one spotted us. When we arrived at the bus depot, instead of going in and purchasing tickets, I hailed an unmarked van and paid him to drive us to the Mexican border. I still remember my brother, who was only 10 years old at the time, laying on the floor of the van with his head held in both hands. The pressure from the stress had gotten to him. I reassured him it would be all right. No one in our family was willing to step forward and take us in, so we had no choice but to flee.

It was a long ride and once we arrived at the border, we jumped out and ran for our lives. Once on the other side of the border, we got into a cab and went to a nearby hotel where we stayed for the night. We called my aunt, who lived in the city, to let her know we were safe and staying at the a Country Club Hotel. I got up that morning and waited to hear from my mother. There was a knock at the door, and I began to feel some sense of promise and thought it might've been our mother. Instead, it was two of our cousins. My aunt had sent them to get us. I was again left disappointed. My siblings and I had risked our lives to escape, and my mom, still wouldn't come out of hiding to get us. I had a hard conversation with my brother and sister.

"If you want to go with mom, go ahead. I've lost all trust in her and I'm going back to L.A." My brother and sister left with my two cousins. I called my friend Adrianne and she drove from Los Alamitos, California, to Mexico to pick me and Libby up.

When I returned to Los Angeles, I went to my father's house only to discover he no longer lived there.

Where was I to go?

The only place I could think of was a friend's house. Her mother was in the same line of work as my mom, so my friend was often home alone and unsupervised.

Once I had settled in a bit, my friend Sandra organized a get-together and invited some friends over. We all drove to a hang-out spot called Elysian Heights. It was there that I met a young man who was 19 years old. He had attended catholic school his entire life and had been a boy scout. As we sat in his car, I began to share with him what was going on. When we went back to my friend's house, we walked into the living room where several people were smoking crack cocaine. I had tried it for the first time the night before, and it felt so good. I wanted more of that. Honestly, I needed more of that.

"It was nice speaking with you, but I think I'll go to the living room and join the others," I said to the young man. Somehow, he kept me engaged long enough that the urge to join them passed. The young man looked at me and said,

"You can't stay here."

He took me home to his parents and asked if I could stay there with them until I found my dad. He and his family lived in Watts, and I figured neither the feds nor anyone in the mafia knew of him and his family, so it was a good place to hide out for a while.

As my theme song and childhood favorite reminded me, *I, I, I, I was staying alive.*

Living with him and his parents was the closest to *normal* I had ever known. His mother was a cosmetics representative, and she regularly had the local priest over for dinner. Her husband was a dedicated father. He worked two jobs to put his children through private school. The Savior, as I called my new friend, was spoiled by his parents, which I suppose I should be grateful for. I don't know many parents who would have taken me in. His mother and her family had lived on the same street since she was 3 years old. She grew up in her mother's house, which was across the street, and where I was to stay. Her mother had passed years prior and the only person living in the house was her eldest daughter. There were two extra bedrooms in the house and his mother offered me one of them under one condition: I had to go back to school and possibly get a part-time job. The rent was to be $40 a month. This was not a bad opportunity at all, and I was starving for normal.

I went back to High School but was informed that the school was overcrowded. I would take the bus to a different school in Van Nuys, which was about 35 miles away. Each morning, The Savior, who had become my boyfriend, would take me to the bus stop and pick me up.

~

It didn't take long before he handed me a set of rules of his own:

1. I wasn't to wear make-up.
2. I wasn't to wear anything that wasn't approved by him.
3. I wasn't to speak to anyone while on the bus or at school.

At first, I thought, *he isn't going to know if I speak to people at school.* Soon after I realized he had someone who followed me and reported back to him. Every day I came home from school to an interrogation session that usually went on for hours. He would search my backpack for evidence of who knows what. One day I remember he found a tissue with some black smudge on it, and he lost it. I had worn a bit of eyeliner and took it off before he picked me up, and this prompted a severe beating.

The Savior turned out to be incredibly jealous, controlling, physically and verbally abusive, and an alcoholic. When we went out, I had to walk with my head down and stare at that floor while he led me by the hand. After he would hit me, his parents would clean me up and take me out to dinner to make up for his behavior. One time he popped me on my lip and the blood went all over my white sweatshirt. His mother and sister waited outside of my room for it all to end then grabbed me, turned my sweatshirt inside out, and said,

"Come on, let's go eat."

This became my new norm. I discovered that their family was just as dysfunctional, but in a different way.

Eventually, my mom resurfaced. She called to tell me she was in Texas with her sister, Anna. She said she was going to leave my brother and sister with Anna while she went back to Mexico to sell a house she had. What mom had failed to mention to me, which I later learned from my brother, was that because mom was a fugitive, they couldn't cross the border like normal citizens. She had a coyote smuggle them across, and my brother, sister, and my mother had to swim across the Colorado River.

I told my mom that I didn't feel comfortable with my sister and brother staying with Aunt Anna, especially after what she had done to her own brothers and sisters when she turned them into social services. I convinced The Savior to drive me to Houston to go get them. I called my aunt to let her know I was coming in three days' time.

We were set to leave when I received a call from my aunt.

"Don't bother coming for your brother and sister," she said. "I turned them into social services."

My heart dropped and I immediately became lightheaded. My aunt had done it again and my mother should have known better! Although The Savior was no walk in the park, more than any other time I needed the stability of a place to stay while I figured out how to get my brother and sister out of foster care.

It took me about two weeks to track my brother and sister down. I became acquainted with their social workers and stayed in regular communication with them both. It broke my heart that my sister and brother had been separated. It was the worst case of *deja vu* as my family's story had repeated itself. The Savior couldn't handle me being at school all day outside of his constant supervision, so he made me quit. One day he walked into the room and handed me a book, "The Test Guide to Taking Your GED." I didn't care that he pulled me out of school as I had bigger problems to worry about than his jealousy.

When I wasn't on the phone with social services finding out what needed to be done to get my brother and sister back, I studied. When the time came for me to take the test, The Savior drove me to the testing center in Downtown L.A. I took the test while he waited outside. I received my results in the mail two weeks later and passed on my first attempt. I had not even completed the 9th grade, but I had my G.E.D.

For a long time, I was ashamed that I had not completed high school nor attended college, but I figured my curriculum was being administered through the Earth School.

Chapter 9
Light in the Tunnel

While out running errands with The Savior's mother on a fall day in 1988, I sat outside in the car with her, parked in front of a grocery store.

"Why don't you go in and apply for a job?" a voice inside me inquired.

Mama, as I called her, thought it was a good idea, so I went into the store and asked to speak with the manager. He handed me an application for a box girl position, and I filled it out. I heard back from the store within days and had been hired. Before I could begin work, I would have to do two things: Sign up with the Local Union in downtown L.A. and get a physical.

The Savior's parents drove me to the nearby hospital for my exam. Once finished, we returned home for lunch. As we all sat at the table, the phone rang. Mama got up to answer it, then handed me the phone. It was the nurse from the hospital.

"Hello?" I responded. "I just wanted to let you know your test came back positive," the nurse said. With a look of confusion on my face, I asked,

"Positive for what?" She hesitated then said,

"You're pregnant."

She went on to say that it would be good if we scheduled an appointment for my prenatal care and said a few other things that blurred out to me. Since Mama and Papa were sitting there, I told the nurse I would have to call her back. I went back to the table in a state of utter confusion and continued with our lunch. I didn't say a word about what I had just discovered. I was in an unstable situation and about to begin a new job that paid minimum wage, which at that time was $3.75 per hour. Most people in a similar predicament would not have thought twice about terminating the pregnancy.

I kept my pregnancy a secret for as long as I could before morning sickness gave me away. One night, I returned to my sleeping quarters after dinner when The Savior and his mother came into my room.

"Are you pregnant?" he asked, to which I said yes. He mentioned something about an abortion, and I said,

"I am not getting rid of my baby."

He and his mother seemed surprised and likely frustrated with my decision. After all, The Savior and I had only been together a little over a year. To sum things up, my mother was a drug dealer who was on the run from the authorities as well as the mafia.

I understood better than anyone that I was not an ideal mate for her son. I needed a place to stay but I was prepared to leave because I was not going to get rid of my child. This decision did not come from a place of my being a 'good Christian' or anything along those lines. It was not often that I spoke or knew something from a deep level of certainty. However, my decision to keep my child came from that certainty.

I was 17 years old at the time and as I counted the months to the arrival of my baby, I figured I would turn 18 just in time. I was hired on at the grocery store and it was my health insurance from my job that covered 100 percent of my prenatal care as well as the birth of my son. I was grateful for this as his father did not have a job or insurance at the time.

My son was born in 1989, a month after I had turned 18. Because of the accident, I had when I was 12 years old and the injuries I sustained, my hips did not expand to make way for the delivery. I was in labor for 33 long hours, and it was painful. The doctors wanted to perform a C-section, but The Savior instructed the doctors not to because I already had enough scars on my body, particularly on my legs. Luckily for me, two nurses were visiting from England, and they came into the room to assist. They had me get on my knees while on the bed. One of the nurses got under one arm and the other nurse got under the other arm. Once in this position, my son's head was dislodged, and they rushed me to the delivery room.

When they placed my son in my arms, I marveled at the bundle of life before me and his long eyelashes. I took in every inch and crevice of my baby. My eyes widened when I looked at his head. It was long like the characters in the movie *The Coneheads*. He was stuck in the birth canal for 33 hours and came out looking like the Pharaoh Akhenaten. The nurse must have noticed my reaction because she quickly informed me the beanie would take care of it and it did.

The Savior disappeared after the birth of our son. I imagine he was out celebrating with his friends. My mother was still in Mexico and Gloria, The Savior's mother, had gone to Northern California to see about her sick aunt. His father was the only one who stayed with me in the hospital throughout much of the experience. At some point, before I went into the delivery room, he held my hand and asked,

"Do you see the trouble you got yourself into?"

I suppose he felt bad for me because of the pain I was in.

None of the women in my life were at home to assist me, so I decided to extend my stay at the hospital for a couple of days. This was during a time when the hospitals didn't kick you out a few hours after delivery.

When I did arrive at the house, my son's grandfather had sanitized the entire house and had a pot of chicken soup going on the stove. It wasn't long before Pete took his new grandson into his arms and

went off to the rocking chair in the den. This is where you would find him from that point forward: In the rocking chair with his grandson.

After we had the baby shower, I moved into the main family home and organized our bedroom with the baby's crib and furniture. The crib was below a vent that ran throughout the house. As soon as my son let out a cry, I didn't lose ant sleep at all because of

Grandpa Pete. Since I didn't breastfeed, Grandpa Pete quickly learned how to prepare my son's bottles of formula. My son and Grandpa Pete had a beautiful bond from the start, and I was grateful for the love he naturally showed my son.

Chapter 10
Family Reunion

My mom had returned but was still in hiding. She ended up staying with the man who had wanted to be with her for years and, finally, he had his chance. This man waited patiently on the sidelines. As their relationship flourished, I continued my communication with the social workers. They emphasized that I could not apply for custody of my siblings since I wasn't of legal age when I began the process. This went on for a year and a half. Tired and ready to be with my siblings, I began to look for someone to stand in as proxy.

Eventually, I tracked my father down and he was not in good shape. The crack pandemic had hit the poor areas hardest, and my father and his wife had fallen victim to it. Luckily for me, all his communication with my brother's caseworker was over the phone. I explained to dad that I would be the one to take care of my brother. I only needed him on paper to say he would take custody of him, to which he agreed.

The day my brother was taken to my father's home, I rushed over to get him. I didn't even give them a chance to object. My brother would be better off with me, and I would pay rent for him to have a bedroom at the house across the street. I immediately signed my brother up for school and he began the seventh grade. Additionally, I added him to my health insurance at work, so he was taken care of. Occasionally, mom would come and pick him up for the day, but she always brought him back.

Since my sister had a different father from my brother and me, social services refused to release her to my father, but not for lack of trying. I was so frustrated. No one would agree to sponsor her until her aunt and uncle from her father's side finally stepped in. The agreement was to be like the one I had with my father. When I went to retrieve her, her aunt and uncle had changed their minds. They thought I was too young to take care of two siblings and a new baby. It broke my heart that I had to come home without her.

A few years went by, and Mom constantly expressed her intense sadness. She missed my sister deeply. Despite everything, I felt bad for her. So, one day my friend and I drove to Tijuana to get my sister from her school. I told her we were going home and that we would be a family again. Things with my son's father had never been good so we were off and on all the time. I decided to split from The Savior and purchased a condominium with my mom's now-husband so that we would all live under the same roof.

Chapter 11
It All Falls Down

In 1992, I started working as a receptionist at a law firm in Beverly Hills. I had worked as a box girl at the grocery store for a few years and knew it was time to shift into something that would provide greater pay, better benefits, and a better life for my family and me.

As I was soon to find out, old problems die hard and if not addressed, will resurface until dealt with. One day, while at my desk, the phone rang. I answered and on the other end was a federal agent.

"We are arresting your mother and we wanted to let you know so you can come and pick up your son," he said. I slammed the phone down but not before asking him,

"How did you know where to find her?" He then replied,

"So you knew your mother was a fugitive?"

I hung up the phone and rushed home. Mom was taken to the Metropolitan Detention Center in Los Angeles. Someone in her inner circle had turned her in.

My stepfather, brother, sister, and I headed downtown as my mom was scheduled to appear before the judge that day. We settled in the courtroom and a few minutes later, the judge appeared and immediately began to address my mother.

"You are very fortunate that I am not going to put you away for years. I see your family is here," he said. He then asked,

"Have you changed your ways?"

My mom, with her head slightly lowered, responded,

"Yes, your honor."

The judge looked my mom over before giving his verdict.

"I am going to give you one more chance, but don't ever let me see you in my courtroom again," he said. My mom was released that day.

I had prayed that things would change with my mom, but they didn't. Despite everything, mom was still incredibly difficult to live with. One day after a physical altercation, I packed up my things and went back to live with my son's father. I was metaphorically and even physically between a rock and a hard place. Honestly, when it came to my mother and my son's father, I felt like I was dealing with the same personality, only in different bodies.

One day as I sat in my room over at my son's father's house, a friend called and invited me over. It wasn't often that I got to visit this friend, so I agreed to meet up with her. During my visit, she told me about something new she had discovered and how great it was. It sounded like a good time and would help take my mind off of everything that was happening in my life, so I tried it with her. The new thing was called crystal meth. Within minutes, I felt a surge of energy and was no longer hungry. I was hooked immediately. Crystal meth also allowed me to tap into a level of courage that I had not previously felt. I would no longer sit and allow The Savior to beat me anymore. I would no longer silently shield myself from his rage-filled blows. No more. He would have a fight on his hands.

The Savior had begun to lose his control over me, and he didn't like it one bit. I wanted to move out of his parent's home and after so many nights of arguments, he gave in. We went to look at apartments and found a lovely place in the neighboring city of Downey. We moved in but it didn't last long.

I used crystal meth regularly and it had taken a huge toll on our relationship. I was tired of being his possession and wanted to come out from his iron fist. With time, The Savior grew weary of my rebellion and moved out while I was at work. When I returned home later that day and set the grocery bag down on what normally was the coffee table, it fell straight to the floor. All the furniture, and The Savior, were gone. He had returned home to his parents.

In November 1993, I lost my job at the law firm, turned in my apartment, and went to live with a friend. One night, during a get-together, I consumed crystal meth, LSD, cocaine, and alcohol. I was having a hard time staying grounded and I began to freak out. I didn't want to be around anyone, so I retreated to my room. Luckily, my brother showed up. He asked me what was wrong, and I told him what I had done. He stayed with me that entire night. If it weren't for my brother coming over that night and staying with me, I'm convinced I would have lost my mind and untethered completely.

For the next three days, I walked around in somewhat of an altered state. Everything spoke to me about

God. I saw the interconnectedness of all of life and how it communicated with us.

While out on an errand, I stopped at a railroad crossing and waited for the train to pass. As I waited, I had a vision and in it, I was older. If I had to guess, I would say I was in my forties. I stood in a pulpit that was covered in purple carpet. From what I could tell, I was ministering to a congregation. When the train passed, I snapped out of the vision and continued making my way home. Once home, I laid down on the bed and turned on the radio, which was tuned to a Christian radio station. I usually didn't listen to that type of music, but I left it on the station. The man on the radio shared a story about Moses. God had asked Moses to lead his people out of Egypt. Moses responded,

"...but God, I wouldn't know what to say to lead my people." God told Moses,

"When the time comes it is I who will speak through you."

The following day, one of our roommates read Tarot cards for me. She informed me someone would be taken out of her position due to an 'illness' or something along those lines, and I would be asked to step in. That evening, my friend's mother shared with me that her son and daughter-in-law had just purchased a home a couple of counties over. The person who was to be a live-in nanny had just discovered she was pregnant and would not be moving in with them. Both her son and daughter-in-law worked in Los Angeles and needed to commute to be able to afford their new home. Her son was a sheriff.

What better place for me to be than under the supervision of a sheriff?

I desperately wanted to get sober. I quickly informed her that I would gladly move in with them and be their nanny by day if I could go to school at night. For the next two years, I stayed with them while I worked on my paralegal certificate at night. I also wanted to prove to my son's father and his family that I had gotten my life together and could be a good mother.

I graduated from paralegal studies in 1996 and returned to The Savior's home. I did not yet have it in me to try life on my own. More than anything, I wanted to be under the same roof as my son.

Chapter 12
An Awakening is Happening

I n 1997, I was offered a receptionist position at a Downtown Los Angeles law firm. I had decided to move back to L.A. and work things out with the savior. I missed my son and it seemed if I wanted to be with him, his father was part of the deal. At the time I was commuting daily to Fontana (a suburb of San Bernardino County), and it was not an easy commute, which is what prompted the job search.

Within a few months of being hired at the firm, a legal secretary position opened. Cecilia, one of the legal secretaries encouraged me to apply for it and her confidence in me gave me confidence in myself. She agreed to train me on all things Legal Secretary each day after work and was very knowledgeable, so I decided to apply for the position. The Partner I would be working for seemed like a nice person and I was excited to give it a try. It almost felt like an agreement made between he and me and just like that I had the job. Not long after accepting the position I noticed my boss had been quiet for a few days and had not asked me for much. Turns out he and another attorney were opening their own law office and had been busy making arrangements. When my boss asked if I would be interested in joining them, I was taken aback by how quickly things were progressing in my professional life. I wanted to say yes right away and there was one thing I had to take care of before I could join them on their new venture: I had to marry my son's father. You see, the week prior, my son's father he had given me an ultimatum. He told me either I marry him or move out. I had been sitting with the decision whether to stay or try life on my own and in fact, was leaning in the direction of leaving him when my boss offered me the opportunity to join him.

Implementing this level of change in both my personal and professional life felt like too much to handle at once so I decided to marry and let that part of my life remain for now so I could give this new position the attention it would require. My boss must have gotten a sense of my lack of enthusiasm to get married and jokingly offered to have a getaway car parked outside of the church should I change my mind. I knew I could not change it at this time.

We organized the wedding quickly and decided to wed the last weekend of February 1998. We drove to

Las Vegas and had our immediate family join us. It was not how I had envisioned my wedding, but to be honest, I had not spent much time contemplating getting married. Life, until this point had been focused on surviving.

I was now 28 years old, about to get married and managing a small law firm. Not bad considering what my life circumstances had been five years prior. I was proud of my professional and personal progress. I had overcome a lot, but perhaps that was the issue. I had moved over and around the experiences and trauma not necessarily healed from it all AND this was as close to a 'normal' life as I had dared to imagine. It felt good to be a part of something from the beginning as I visualized the firm growing and what it would become.

The hours were long, the court filings were stressful, and I had to learn a lot on the spot. It was sink or swim situation and I was an excellent swimmer. These two men took a chance on me, and I wasn't about to let them down. Their faith in me meant a lot. Everything I learned while at this firm, allowed me to handle a case from beginning to end through litigation, discovery, mediation, and trial. I also learned how the ins and outs of running an office from processing payroll, doing the billing, coordinating benefits, and handling the day-to-day responsibilities of running an office. I was overworked at times, but I didn't mind. Working hard was in my nature and it allowed me to not be at home as much. Doing my job well meant I had proved everyone wrong.

As the firm grew, I needed help and we hired a woman who I became close friends with. I wasn't allowed to have friends outside of work as it would upset the Savior, but he could not tell me what to do while I was at the office. It didn't take her long to notice my home life was less than ideal. No sooner would I walk through the doors each morning then my mother would begin calling and demand to speak to me. Usually, it was to argue or complain about someone or something. Anne had noticed how upset I would get and one morning she said,

"Let me get it."

She told my mom I was not available to talk. My mom was surprised and furious! I had not realized, not speaking with mom was even an option and this was a game changer. One day Anne invited me to go with her to a spiritual psychology class at her church. I had always wanted to go to counseling. I knew my husband would not approve of me going, and I decided to throw caution to the wind and went with her anyway. During the class, the instructor spoke about something called 'triangulating' as a dynamic. Triangulation happens when an individual has an issue with one person but speaks to someone else about the problem instead of speaking directly to person with whom the issue is being had. I instantly recognized the pattern and how it has been playing out in my life and relationships and I was exhausted.

At the time, my sister was staying with us and after the painful ordeal she went through of having been placed in a foster home, I needed to make life easier for her. It took a lot to convince the Savior to allow her to come and stay with us. Each time my husband had a complaint about her (which was often), I would immediately respond with,

"I'll take care of it".

The same thing played out at work. Anytime the partners were upset with one of the attorneys or staff members, I would listen to and then address it with the individual. I was like Mother Theresa or something. I didn't want anyone to be mistreated or was it that I simply didn't like conflict? I think it was the latter. My husband, boss and mother all had a volatile temper, which caused me to walk on eggshells. I didn't want to set them off because the consequences were not ones that I wanted to face or experience. I was so co-dependent and didn't even know it.

As I was being exposed to this new information, I couldn't help but to begin to examine my life. One night as I laid in bed next to my husband, I realized how horrible it felt to be this close in proximity to someone and feel so completely alone. Throughout the years I had contemplated suicide often. It seemed to be a program that had been running in the background. I desperately wanted to be happy, but most of my experiences were not that. In the moments when I would find myself having fun, experiencing joy, or even experiencing a level of peace, it seemed someone would come along and snatch right out from under me with some crazy outburst. It felt as though I simply was not allowed to enjoy life.

One day while at our son's softball game, I was reading *'A Conversation with God'* by Neal Donald Walsh when the following sentence popped off the page,

> *"…who you meet at 20 may not be who you need at 40 if the two of you have not grown together."*

I slammed the book shut and placed my hand over my forehead as if my husband could hear my thoughts. I didn't want him to see the words on the page. I opened the book again and Neal continued,

> *"it is okay to divorce."*

Divorce?! Divorce never occurred to me as an option. It's not because I wasn't aware of it but because over the years every time I expressed my desire to part ways, my husband would respond with,

"The only way you are leaving here is feet first."

And besides, I had gotten myself together personally and professionally and financially. I paid for half of everything in the home. I had become a bit of a commodity, and he wasn't going to let me go easily.

After my drug experience in 1993, something in me opened and I began to explore the deeper meaning of Life. I began reading and devouring every spiritual and self-help book I could get my hands on. I loved going to book stores and discovering these treasures. This and going to the movies by myself were 'my time' activities. I began to question the status quo and my husband was not happy. He wasn't the only one who was unhappy with who I was becoming. I was developing quickly, and no one was happy about that except me.

Working in a law firm was incredibly stressful. Being in a toxic marriage I had outgrown was killing me. Not being allowed to express myself was detrimental. Being surrounded by toxic personalities was exhausting. Up until that point, I had become a highly functioning, codependent individual who had no real idea of who she truly was. 'Codependent', as the Merriam-Webster Dictionary defines it, is a psychological condition or a relationship in which a person is controlled or manipulated by another who is affected with a pathological condition (such as an addiction).

I had been under the control of so many people in my life: my mother, my husband, my family, my friends, and my job. But no more. I was ready to depend on something greater within me.

Chapter 13
A Spiritual Retreat

Our small law firm had grown from an office of three people to fifteen people. Business had been going very well which translated to a lot of work for everyone. In fact, business was so good that one of my bosses purchased a brand-new home in an exclusive area of Rancho Palos Verdes. It was supposed to be a gated community, but each day my boss would come into the office fuming because of the 'riff raff' he saw playing soccer in front of his very expensive home. This prompted him to sue the developer and I was his main support during this intense litigation.

One night while working late, the idea of a spiritual retreat popped into my mind, and I researched it online. I was surprised to find there was such a thing. I found one in Fiji where the bungalows were over the water. There was also a company in Sedona and one in New York, which I had seen on television. Everyone was opposed to the idea of me going on a spiritual retreat: My bosses, my husband, and my family. What they didn't know was that after all, I had been through, I was at the end of my rope and extremely unhappy.

In fact, I was suicidal.

A spiritual retreat was an attempt to shift this. My husband and I compromised on the closest location, so I went to Sedona, Arizona, on an 11-day spiritual retreat.

Sedona is known for its beautiful landscape and its vortexes, or swirling centers of energy that are conducive to healing, meditation, and self-exploration. Vortex points are places where the Earth seems especially alive with energy. Many people feel inspired, recharged, or uplifted after visiting a vortex. Although all of Sedona is a vortex, there are specific sites where the energy is more intense. The four best-known Sedona vortexes are found at Airport Mesa, Cathedral Rock, Bell Rock, and Boynton Canyon — each pulsating with its own energy. Some are thought to produce an upward flow of energy upward while the other sites produce a downward flow of energy, into the Earth.

I arrived in Sedona on a late January evening in 2002. Debra, the owner of the retreat, came by the guest house I stayed in and took me over to her place for my first session.

During the retreat, I saw one to two different healers daily and hiked or rested in between sessions. Each healer I met with had a unique specialty. I saw a spiritual psychologist, an Angel Intuitive, Breathwork Specialist, Massage Therapist, and many more. All of it was new to me and deepened my desire to learn more about the reality of life.

Below are a few of the modalities I worked with while in Sedona:

Holotropic Breathwork

Holotropic Breathwork has become increasingly popular, especially among those who desire to explore a unique process of self-healing to attain a state of wholeness. This practice was developed by psychiatrists Stanislav Grof and Christina Grof in the 1970s to achieve altered states of consciousness (without using drugs) as a potential therapeutic tool.

After entering the session room, I was instantly captivated by the amazing view of Sedona's landscape. The facilitator instructed me to lie down on a mat and to begin breathing deeply.

"In through your nose, out through your mouth. Continue to focus on your breathing."

Before long, I was off on a journey and soaring through the canyons of Sedona. I could not believe what I was experiencing. I was flying through Sedona's red rocks and could feel the wind on my face. I could feel the vortex energy pulsating and infusing the air all around me. Just as I was enjoying myself, I locked eyes with a fire-breathing dragon and a chase ensued. We both zipped in and out of the canyons. When I came to, I was a bit out of breath, and I shared with Tom what I had experienced. I told him that the dragon represented my mother and the nature of our relationship. He said there were times during the session that my body was levitating off the ground.

I had a few more sessions with Tom after my initial breathwork experience. During one session, as soon as I started breathing, I arrived at what felt like a huge, golden, light of love. It felt so good that I stayed in that light for the entire session. When I came to, I told Tom that compared to my first session – which was full of activity – that the second one was peace and light-filled. We walked out of the room to the living room, and he shared my experience with his partner. His response was,

"Oh – you reached Nirvana."

At this point, I didn't know much about Nirvana other than it was a desired state and I was grateful for my brief visit.

Shamanic Astrology

Shamanic Astrology was developed by Daniel Giamario and is an Earth-centered and archetypal approach with a strong emphasis on soul purpose. This system is a study of intent designed to empower our lives based on the Law of Correspondence, '*As Above, So Below*'.

I met with a certified Shamanic Astrologer who prepared my birth and natal chart reports. As he began to describe what he saw based on my chart, he said,

"I see that what you long for is freedom. Let's see… you were supposed to have left your marriage here, and here, and here and here."

He went back a couple of years and showed me where the cosmology had provided windows of opportunities to exit. It was apparent to both of us I had overstayed my welcome and was currently working up the courage to venture out on my own.

Angelic Healing

Angelic Healing is a form of energy healing that helps remove blocks in our energy fields. Some of those blocks include anger, fear, pain, resentment, or anything that is not in true alignment with who we are. Through Angelic Healing, we can remove or loosen those blocks so that we are back in a natural state of flow. As a result, we feel more energetic, alive, and aligned with our highest and best selves.

As the name implies, Angelic Healing works through the love and healing of the angels. In Angelic Healing, the angels guide the therapist while she/he works with the client. The therapist is a vessel to let the healing of the angels pass into the client. The therapist is open to this energy and fully guided by the angels.

The moment I walked into the healer's home, I felt at ease. A wave of emotion washed over me as soon as I sat down, and I sobbed uncontrollably. I was releasing deep pain that I had carried in my heart for years. I remember her saying,

"They (the angels) did some work on your heart. They are saying we circumvented a possible heart condition from developing later."

I should not have been surprised that all my repressed emotions influenced my heart. She also mentioned that the angels said I would write a book and work with children.

I saw a different person for my second angel healing, and it was an interesting experience. This one was with a man named Rob Wergin. I walked into his home, and he shared with me that he had just left his corporate job and life back east to return to what he knew he was here to do. Assist individuals heal. Once I settled on the table, I closed my eyes while Rob and the angels did their thing. At some point during the session, the door flew open, and a gust of wind blew into the room. I kept my eyes closed and watched through my third eye as legions of angels entered the room.

Spiritual Psychology

The main duty of a spiritual psychologist is to counsel people and help them achieve spiritual, mental, and emotional wellbeing. Many people who seek help from a spiritual psychologist are going through a spiritual crisis. I had always wanted to see a therapist, lay down on a couch, and talk about my childhood. Therapy was not something anyone in my family or group of friends had sought so it seemed out of the ordinary for me. Finally, after 30 something years of carrying this around, it was my chance to speak with a licensed psychologist and find out whether I was crazy or not. We spoke about my past and present and work and home life. She then led me in a guided meditation, which was a first for me. I shared my burdens in a safe environment for the first time and I began to feel that maybe there was hope for me after all.

Family Constellation

I reached out to a Family Constellation Therapist named Divio and we scheduled a session. Family Constellation Therapy is a method of family therapy, or systemic therapy, where individual persons are positioned (set up) in the room as stand-ins for family members. In this way, the network of relationships within a family can be visualized. Bert Hellinger developed Family Constellation Work. It's a therapeutic process that helps to break destructive family patterns of unhappiness, illness, failure, and addiction. The results are often immediate and life changing. Bert Hellinger was a German psychotherapist who realized that traumatic events such as violent death, abortion, miscarriage, suicide, abuse, and incest didn't die with the people directly affected. These events could echo down through time and can manifest in later generations as chronic illnesses or psychological states of depression, phobias, anxiety, fear, anger, or unfulfilled relationships.

Because of the short notice, Divio was not able to gather the individuals typically recruited to fill in as family members, but the session was still powerful. We placed pillows to represent both my parents and maternal grandparents. When it came time to address my grandfather, I felt compelled to let him know I was on the path to becoming a minister and had decided to walk the path of light. At that moment, a flow of energy dropped down from the heavens and poured through me.

Divio reached out and embraced me as the current caused my body to wobble back and forth. She confirmed it was my grandfather and he was conferring his blessing on me.

Since my initial visit with Divio, I have gone back to see her and participated in a fully 'staffed' session. Additionally, I had a session with her via video link because I wanted to heal my relationship with my son, and it proved to be just as powerful. One of the reasons why I advocate for this work is because I don't want my children, grandchildren, and great-grandchildren to have to continue to struggle with generational issues if they don't have to. Though it may seem unfair to inherit our ancestors' problems and trauma, the family we are born into comes with the 'right' conditions for our potential unfoldment.

I return to Sedona and her vortexes a couple of times per year, and I never tire of its beautiful scenery and energy. Each time I visit, it feels as though my eyes are seeing color for the first time. One of the best gifts Sedona has given me was a safe space for me to release years, and perhaps even lifetimes, of pain, grief, and tears.

After seeing all the different healers, it was time to integrate. Debra and I sat outside on the patio for a debrief. My 11-day stay in Sedona was ending and it was time for me to return home.

"How am I supposed to maintain this level of peace once I return home?" I asked her.

"I have been shown that life is about so much more. Do I go home and quit my job, leave my marriage, and move into a new home?"

She smiled and took my questions in with grace, intention, and love.

"You don't have to uproot every part of your life at once," she said.

"You will know when it is time to go. In the meantime, grow where you are planted, and when you want to access the peace that is present here now, you just return here in your mind."

These words of wisdom were to carry me through the next few years and carry me they did. I returned to Los Angeles ready to start living.

I would no longer settle for just staying alive.

Chapter 14
First Signs of Disease

I was at work when I noticed that something was off with my right hand. As I attempted to type, it became increasingly challenging to hold my hand steady to hit the keys and I could barely write. I went to see my General Practitioner and from there, was referred to a specialist. Although, it was hard for her to point me in the right direction as she didn't know what was going on with my hand.

My initial symptoms included:

1. Hand numbness.
2. Wrists drop, loss of mobility in my right hand, arm, and shoulder.
3. Weakness throughout the body.
4. Muscle tightness.
5. Falling for no apparent reason.
6. Difficulty walking.

7. Pain throughout my body.
8. Intense fatigue.
9. Difficulty breathing.

I saw countless doctors during a two-year period when I was finally referred to a neurologist affiliated with a hospital in Pasadena. This was a reputable place and I hoped he could figure out what was going on with me. He performed several electromyogram (EMG) tests and electrical testing of nerves and muscles.

During the exams, the doctor inserted needles into my muscles and would run current, which was a little like shock therapy, and it was very uncomfortable. I felt like I was being tortured. The test was supposed to show where the conduction blocks were occurring, which didn't completely make sense to me.

If he had done the test once and knew where the current was unable to pass, why did he continue to conduct this painful test numerous times?

As we continued our consult, he sent me to the hospital for a full-body MRI. Later, he performed a lumbar puncture or spinal tap, and it went terribly wrong. To make matters worse, he performed the procedure right before Thanksgiving 2004. I needed someone to drive me to and from the doctor's office and I abhorred asking anyone for help, but I did it. I asked my friend and co-worker Melinda if she could drop me off and pick me up. I was a little stressed because I didn't know how our bosses would feel about both of us being out of the office at the same time.

Once she dropped me off at home after the procedure, my head began to hurt something awful. Every time I lifted my head off the pillow, it felt as though my head was going to explode.

I called the doctor's office the next day and explained what was happening. They told me there was nothing that could be done as my doctor had left for New Jersey to be with his family for Thanksgiving. I cried, pleaded, and begged for them to find a doctor I could speak to as the pain was unbearable. I think they knew it was a lumbar puncture gone wrong, and no doctor wanted to fix another doctor's mess. After missing work for a couple of days, my boss called to check in on me and when I started crying uncontrollably, he got on the phone with the facility where the procedure had taken place and, in his lawyer voice, got someone to agree to see me.

It was my first Thanksgiving after having split from my husband and he was the last person I wanted to ask for help, but I had no choice. I couldn't drive and needed someone to take me to and from the doctor's office. Thankfully, he agreed to drive me. I grabbed my pillow and climbed into his back seat. I had to lie down the whole way there as any semblance of being upright caused unbearable pain. When I arrived, it was instantly apparent that the clot that had been put in place to prevent the spinal fluid from leaking had not worked and so they took some more blood and plugged the leak at the base of my spine. The reason why my head hurt so badly was because there was no fluid in my skull. My brain was literally sitting on my skull.

When the doctor returned from his holiday, I went in for the results. He said everything appeared normal on the test and wondered if I didn't suffer from depression? He then asked me if I had fallen asleep with my arm over a chair, which cut off the blood flow to my wrist. I was flabbergasted. I explained to him I did not have depression, but I was beginning to feel depressed because of his inability to diagnose the problem.

One morning as I was finishing up my workout and getting dressed in the gym, I overheard a friend talking about a co-worker of hers. The woman's daughter had been ill and none of the doctors in Los Angeles had been able to diagnose her. The woman purchased an R.V., grabbed her daughter, and they drove to the a specialist Clinic in Cleveland. They parked the R.V. in the parking lot of the hospital until someone was able to assist. I was inspired by her proactiveness. When I got to work that morning, I began researching the Clinic. I was surprised to find out they had a location in Scottsdale, Arizona. While on their website I made an appointment, but I would have to wait three months to be seen.

The weekend before it was time to depart for Scottsdale, I went shopping for some CDs to listen to on the drive. The following Monday I got in my car and drove to Scottsdale with my one working hand. The convenience of it all was amazing. I stayed in the a hotel which was directly across the street from the Clinic. This made it very easy to walk back and forth.

I was incredibly nervous the morning of my appointment as I waited to meet the doctor who was assigned to my case. I walked into the consultation room, and he extended his hand and then said,

"I am Dr. Goodman." I

was very pleased to meet him and hoped he would live up to his name 'good man.' I explained what I had experienced and that I only had five days for him to figure out what was going on with me as that was all the time I could take off from work. Between all my doctor's appointments and the botched lumbar puncture, I had missed quite a bit of work and my boss was not very happy with me.

We began a series of tests right away and took what Dr. Goodman referred to as a 'process of elimination' approach.

By the end of the fourth day, this good man said he was certain he had a diagnosis for me but all he could tell me was that it was autoimmune related. He would have more information and a plan of action for me the following morning. As I walked back to the hotel, I called my husband and told him what the doctor had said. I was nervous because the only autoimmune disease I knew of at that time was what Easy E had contracted and died from – A.I.D.S. As I shared with my husband what the doctor said, his voice began to shake and he blurted out,

"I am so sorry I cheated on you."

Never in my wildest imagination had I thought he would cheat on me. His confession came as a surprise, and I had just been handed a 'get out of jail free' card.

The following morning, I went to see Dr. Goodman for my exit interview and to receive instructions on our plan of action. He went on to tell me the official diagnosis was Multi-Focal Motor Neuropathy. Admittedly, I was relieved, and to be clear I asked,

"I don't have A.I.D.S?"

Dr. Goodman chuckled and said no. He explained how this condition progresses and that I could treat it one of two ways. The first option was to receive monthly, steroid injections, and the second was a plasma-derived product which I understood to be the more natural of the two. He went on to tell me that he had decided for me to follow up with a neurologist in Los Angeles. He informed me the doctor was the No. 1 neurologist in the country and that I would be in excellent hands.

Multifocal Motor Neuropathy (MMN) is a disease that affects your body's motor nerves, which are the nerves that control your muscles. The condition makes it hard for the motor nerves to send the electrical signals that move your body, which causes your hands and arms to feel weak. They'll also twitch and cramp. MMN is not life-threatening, and, in most cases, treatments can make the muscles stronger. The disease can get worse slowly, and after a while, one may have a hard time doing daily tasks like typing or getting dressed. But for many people, symptoms may be so mild that they don't need treatment at all. One may be able to work and stay active for many years after diagnosis. Most people are diagnosed with MMN in their 40s and 50s, although adults from ages 20 to 80 can find out they have the disease as well.

No one knows what causes MMN.

Scientists do know it is an autoimmune disease, meaning the immune system mistakenly attacks the nerve cells as if they were invaders. Researchers are studying the disease to understand why it happens. My first symptoms were in my hands and lower arms. The muscles felt weak and would cramp up and twitch in a way I couldn't control. It started in specific parts of the right arm, hand, wrist, and fingers. Usually, the symptoms were more severe on one side of my body. The disease can eventually affect the legs. MMN isn't too painful, and I can still feel with my hands and arms because the sensory nerves are not affected; however, symptoms can get worse as I get older, or so I've been told.

My doctor prescribed a medication called Intravenous Immunoglobulin (IVIg). I get the drug intravenously twice a month every four weeks. Luckily for me, I have a nurse who comes to my home and administers it for me. Many people with MMN can continue most or at least some of their normal activities. As the condition progresses, it can interfere with daily tasks. When my hand muscles are weak, I may have trouble eating, typing, writing, or buttoning clothes. When my leg muscles are affected, I have trouble walking or standing for long periods of time.

After being diagnosed, I was afraid and relieved simultaneously. I was grateful that I at least knew what was happening to me physically. The next step was to check in to hospital in LA for three days while I received the initial IVIg infusion. Luckily for me, my friends and family kept me company. The reason why I had to go to the hospital to have the medicine administered was because a potential side effect was cardiac arrest.

Before I went to the Clinic, I reached out to a friend. The plan was that after I finished at the Clinic, I would drive myself to his place in Colorado. When the time came, Rob who I had worked with in Sedona and had since relocated, had me sit up on his table and began a form of energy healing. He placed one hand over my heart and one on my back and started to pull stuff from me energetically.

"What have you been thinking?" he asked.

I was surprised by his question. He was the first person to bring self-awareness to my attention. For years, I had bottled up most of my emotions and I prided myself in not allowing others to know how I felt. Yet there was this man who was able to sense the volcano of emotions just beneath the surface.

When I arrived home from Colorado, I explained to my husband that I could no longer be in the marriage, and for the first time he responded with,

"If you want to leave, go ahead. I won't stop you."

Within a few days, I found an apartment near my son's high school, packed a few of my belongings, and I was gone. I used what I had in my 401k and was able to set up a home of my own for the first time in my life. I was 34 years old and for the first time, I felt safe in my own home.

Shortly after I moved into my apartment, my husband's co-worker came over for a visit.

"I'm sorry to do this Miss Cyndi," he said, then handed me an 8" x 11" envelope.

My husband had filed for divorce. I was happy to be free of him and at the same time, I saw how selfish he was. He knew I needed the double insurance coverage, but that was why it was better we divorced.

Just like that, an 18-year relationship was done. I later discovered that his current girlfriend had prepared the divorce papers.

Honestly, had it not been for the condition showing up when it did, I would not have had the courage to leave that relationship. I would not have stopped running out my door every time someone called and asked for help. In a way, I feel the condition was a catalyst for tremendous change, growth, and healing and I am grateful to it.

Chapter 15
Getting to the Root

My healing journey prompted me to slow down and notice the intricacies of my day-to-day life that might be contributing to the condition and symptoms I was experiencing. Upon some introspection, I realized that my symptoms started to appear in 2002, shortly after my dentist appointment. I had gone in for a regular teeth cleaning. While there, the dentist shared with me that he could remove my mercury fillings and replace them with a much more aesthetically pleasing white material. I hadn't given it any prior thought, but it seemed like an OK idea. Shortly after he completed that procedure, the symptoms began. It wasn't until a few years later, when I came across a documentary on the dangers of mercury fillings, that I began to put two and two together. I also learned that the improper removal of mercury fillings was even more dangerous than the fillings, especially if not removed by a holistically trained dentist. My dentist had not taken the necessary precautions nor was he trained in holistically removing amalgam fillings. According to the video, mercury fillings release toxic gases into our system constantly; however, the improper removal of the fillings would cause a larger release of toxic gases, which could severely impact the patient's nervous system.

Amalgam fillings, also called silver fillings, have been used in dentistry for more than a century. When they were first used, the FDA was not required to test them for safety but that has changed. Today, mercury is considered by the World Health Organization (WHO) as one of the top ten chemicals or groups of chemicals of major public health concern and yet, they are still used in dental work every day. A 2011 risk assessment estimated that 122 million Americans have gotten higher doses of mercury than the safety threshold, likely from their dental fillings. Believe it or not, mercury fillings have been a political debate for decades and are banned in other countries; however, they are still being used in the United States. This whole process has shown me the importance of being proactive with my health. I have discovered it is up to the patient to conduct the research and exercise discernment before blindly agreeing to any type of procedure or medication that a doctor or specialist recommends.

As I continued my IVIg treatments, I researched other ways to support my body in healing. One of the things I noticed was that most of the food I had consumed in life was not healthy for me. I had just lost 60 pounds while on a fad diet but at no point during the diet did I become aware of the importance of eating organic, whole foods. Up until then, my diet consisted of mostly animal protein, dairy, and vegetables and none of it was organic or grass-fed. When we consume animal protein, and it is not labeled as 'Grass-Fed' or 'Hormone or Antibiotic Free', then we consume what the animal consumed, which is usually genetically modified organism (GMO) corn. We also consume the injections that are given to the animals to ward off bacteria as it remains in their flesh.

So, *what is a GMO?* According to Webster's Dictionary, a genetically modified organism (GMO) is any organism whose genetic material has been altered using genetic engineering techniques. The exact definition of a genetically modified organism and what constitutes genetic engineering varies, with the most common being an organism altered in a way that 'does not occur naturally by mating and/or natural recombination.' A wide variety of organisms have been genetically modified, from animals to plants and microorganisms. Genes have been transferred within the same species, across species (creating transgenic organisms), and even across kingdoms. New genes can be introduced, or endogenous genes can be enhanced, altered, or knocked out.

Some studies show that GMO products are harmful to the gut biodome, which leads to a syndrome called leaky gut. Leaky gut occurs when non-digestible foods lacerate the stomach lining, then enter the bloodstream, contributing to an array of autoimmune diseases. Mostly all GMO products are designed to withstand herbicides such as weed killer which can cause cancer. Additionally, GMO corn is used to feed chicken, cattle, pigs, fish, etc.

So, even if you buy organic fruits and vegetables, you should make sure: a) Your fish is wild-caught; b) Your poultry is organic and free-range; and c) Your beef is grass feed, organic, natural, and hormone-free.

It is best for our bodies if we consume foods as close to their natural state as possible. It is even more essential, in my opinion, that we stay clear of processed foods. I believe that if one wants to be healthy, he or she must eat healthily.

I was taking the steps to get my physical body in order and had to take bold steps to harmonize my work environment. In 2006, I applied for a position at a larger law firm after running the small boutique firm since 1998. I interviewed for a supportive administrative role, which meant a significant pay cut. It took a year to get my foot in the door, and I had to agree to making $10,000 less than I was used to, but I was ready. I needed less stress. I had already left the toxic marriage, and it was time for an 'easier' job.

Saying goodbye to my boss was like saying goodbye to a dear mentor. He was such a part of my life and family, and that job had provided me with a chance to build my life in ways that other jobs hadn't. It helped me become self-sufficient and showed me my many skills and abilities. I knew he was sad to see me go but my departure was something I had to do for my physical and mental well-being.

Over the years, I implemented changes that reduced my stress levels even more. For one, I stopped taking all my mother's calls. This did not go over well with her. When I didn't answer my cell or desk phone, she would call the receptionist. My mom had no idea what boundaries were. It had gotten so bad that the staff asked my mother to stop calling; they couldn't deal with her harassment. This had been a pattern over the years: When she was upset with me, she would call my job and attempt to get me fired.

On top of that, many people didn't know about my diagnosis. I desperately attempted to keep up with everyone else while being 'handicapped'. Anytime my job wanted me to work 12-hour days and weekends to support huge cases, I found a way to get out of it. I knew that physically I could not handle the workload. Besides spending eight hours a day in the office, I spent an average of three hours a day commuting to and from work. None of it was ideal and yet I managed to keep calm amidst the stress.

Chapter 16
The DUI

I was starting to feel some sense of balance in my life when I made one decision that I'd have to pay for later. A friend of mine was celebrating her birthday with a party and the location was a couple of miles from me. I went shopping earlier in the day with my mother and sister and hadn't eaten all that day. When I arrived at the party, I took a couple of shots with friends, and then we walked across the parking lot into the club. The music was blaring, and everybody was feeling good. We started dancing and I ordered one more drink. Shortly after, security escorted us to a different section of the club as the area we were in was closing for the night.

Somehow, I ended up outside in the parking lot. A gust of wind hit me, and I got in my car. I began making my way to the local bar where my friends hang out, but I never made it there. As I drove down

Ocean Boulevard, I must have passed out. I was awakened by a thud and a jolting sensation. I had side-swiped a couple of cars. I saw a side street and decided to park there to assess the damage. As I turned the corner, an officer stood with his hand outstretched, and he motioned for me to stop.

The officer came over to the driver's side and opened my door. He helped me out of the car and walked me over to the patrol car, where he placed me in the back of his car.

"Are you taking me home?" I asked.

"No, I'm taking you to the hospital to get checked," he responded. "Then, I'm taking you to jail."

I begged him not to do that but there was no talking my way out of that situation. While in the hospital, I mentioned to one of the officers that I was due for treatment on Tuesday, but he didn't care. Once I was finished at the hospital, I was taken to the jail where I was processed and placed inside a holding cell.

As I slept off the alcohol for the first 24 hours, I stayed curled up in a corner. Occasionally, I looked up and around and noticed most of the women in the cell were likely in for prostitution. I shook my head in utter shame; I couldn't believe I had gotten myself into this predicament. I was there for two whole days before I noticed there a phone on the wall. I called the only number I knew by heart, which was my friend Adrianne, and she let my son know what had happened. That was the worst feeling in the world.

When the time came to appear in court, the individuals whose cars I had damaged showed up for reparations. They speculated out loud with each other as to who they thought the perpetrator was and how he must've looked. They had no idea the person they were speculating about was me, the woman who stood next to them. We entered the courtroom, I sat down, and the victims sat behind me. When the judge called my name, a gasp rang through the courtroom. They couldn't believe the perpetrator was someone who looked like me. The judge was kind and stern simultaneously. He imposed a $10,000 fine, DUI classes, Alcoholics Anonymous classes, and 200 hours of community service.

As a self-punishment, I made myself take the bus to and from work instead of getting the restricted license. I wanted to ensure I learned my lesson. I wanted to ensure I never did that again. I rode my beach cruiser to my classes and meetings for six months. While attending the DUI classes, I was surprised to learn that there were individuals there who had gotten three DUIs in a period of 90 days. I was determined that I wouldn't be a repeat offender.

Chapter 17
Cleaning House

"**M**om, we are going to that French restaurant you've always wanted to try," my son said to me one day in May 2008. My birthday was approaching, and he knew how much I wanted to go to that restaurant. When I picked him up, I was surprised that his girlfriend was with him and would be joining us, but I didn't give it a second thought. We drove to the restaurant and talked the whole way, and I was happy to be spending time with them. Once inside the restaurant and after we ordered our food, I watched as my son and his girlfriend joined hands.

"We have something to tell you," they said.

In that moment, the sound went out in my ears. I looked around the restaurant and saw everyone's lips moving, waiters serving, and yet I couldn't hear anything. I turned back to my son and his girlfriend and watched their lips as they said,

"We are having a baby."

I leaned back in my seat, shook my head to see if I could get my hearing back, and there it was.

"Did you say what I think you said?" I asked.

"You are going to be a grandmother," they continued.

But I am only 37 years old, I thought. *Who's a grandmother at 37 years old?*

I mean, I had just started dating.

My granddaughter, Natasha, arrived on the evening of her baby shower, two months before her due date. She was born weighing 1½ pounds with a hole in her heart and underdeveloped lungs and was in the intensive care unit for a couple of months. When I wasn't working, I was at the hospital visiting her. I nicknamed her 'Little Foot' because she was so tiny. While in the incubator, she was hooked up to monitoring devices and her eyes were covered. One day, she reached her little handout and squeezed my index finger. It was like although she couldn't see me, she could feel my presence. At that point, I was hers.

When we brought her home, Natasha had a monitor attached to her heart that notified us when her heart stopped. This usually happened during a feeding. We were all trained to place our hand on her back and massage the heart, which would get it going again and the monitor would turn off.

This little girl was going to require our undivided attention. She cleaned house in my personal life and didn't even ask for permission. I was beginning to think that for a tiny person she was powerful.

Natasha and I hung out a lot on the weekends during the first couple of years of her life. She was sunshine on a cloudy day. Anytime there was overcast, she'd put on her bathing suit, sit on the living room floor, and have a picnic. She revitalized my life in every possible way; however, this did not occur without some resistance on my part. I was 38 years old when Natasha was born, and since she had so many health issues, I primarily assisted my son and his girlfriend in taking care of her. As a result, I didn't have a personal life, which was probably for the best. The men I dated at that time weren't the best.

It is said that children will lead the way and as an adult, I thought I knew better. I simply had not realized yet that I was sitting before a master teacher. One of the things I had struggled with at the time was issues of worthiness. I didn't feel worthy of people's love and here was this beautiful Earth angel who was loving me for simply being her Nana.

Chapter 18
Finding Home

My brother and I wanted to start 2011 off on a higher note, so we met, along with his wife, for a New Year's Day hike. During our hike, my brother mentioned he felt the desire to attend church but didn't feel drawn to the Catholic church or the Christian church at the time. I shared with him that I had seen a 'church' on a video I received from Spiritual Cinema Circle that had caught my attention. I didn't know where it was, but it was called Agape International Spiritual Center. From what I had seen on the film, the church had an amazing choir and it looked like it was a huge church. I wanted to go but was too shy to go by myself. The purpose of our hike was to start the year off on the 'right foot' and now we were planning on attending church together the following week. So far, so good.

I had never considered myself a member of any religious organization as I never resonated with any church. I don't know what it was, but I felt drawn to Agape for a long time. I had received that film from Spiritual Cinema Circle in 2007 and four years later, I was still intrigued. I figured it took me a while to attend because it just wasn't my time. When I finally did an online search of Agape and realized it was in Culver City, I nearly fell out of my chair. It was practically in my backyard. I had been traveling to Sedona for three years and now I had Agape, which would be a much closer commute.

My brother, sister-in-law, and I walked into Agape for the first time the second week of January 2011. I was shocked. I remembered a vision I had back in 1993 while stopped at the train tracks. In the vision, I saw an older version of myself standing near a pulpit on a purple carpeted stage. I didn't know how many churches had purple carpet, but there it was, staring me in the face as if to say, "Welcome home."

We sat to listen to the service, and I had no idea who Rev. Michael was other than seeing him briefly on the video Then something began to happen. Rev. Michael said,

"Turn to someone."

The man sitting in front of my brother turned around and locked eyes with him. My sister-in-law and I must have zoned out when Rev. Michael gave the instructions because we watched in amazement. This young man proceeded to repeat after Rev. Michael to my brother,

"My, my, my – you are an amazing and beautiful being. I see God in you! You were born to deliver your gifts and talents to the world! Let's do this, together! And so, it is, Amen."

We thought what happened was totally random and that this young man had chosen my brother to say these beautiful words to, but this was a part of every service. It was exquisite to have someone see you and speak this truth to you at every service.

Then, Rev. Michael asked all newcomers to stand to receive a blessing from him and the congregation. The congregation repeated after Rev. Michael,

"We see you. We know who you really are. You are a wonderful emanation of God. We appreciate you and we love you."

I purposely didn't turn to look at my brother and sister-in-law because I knew we were all crying.

Carlos and Renee did not stay at Agape, but they continued their spiritual journeys. I felt God used them to deliver me to my spiritual home. Once they knew I was safe inside, their mission was accomplished, and they were able to walk away.

During a March 2011 service, Rev. Michael said,

"Take a class, it will change your life, and don't say I didn't warn you."

That day I went home and thought about my finances. At the time, I made just enough to cover my mortgage, pay my car note and insurance, pay utilities, and buy groceries. This usually left me with a little bit of monthly spending money.

How was I going to afford a $200 class when I was on a tight budget?

When I got home that evening, I realized I could discontinue my cable services as it cost $200 per month. What would I rather do with the money? Take a class that might change my life or watch True Blood on Sunday nights? I decided to get rid of my cable and signed up for my first class.

My first class was 'Transcended Masters' taught by Rev. John Elliot. At the time, it was incredibly difficult for me to leave my house and go to class; not because of lack of time or lack of funds, but because I was painfully shy – I didn't know anyone. When I arrived at class each week, I would sit and listen to Rev. John talk about all these people I had never heard of. The class was about how 'New Thought' came to be and who the key players were.

As Rev. John taught, I would stare at my feet so I wouldn't have to make eye contact with anyone. Then one day, the gentlemen who sat next to me every week tapped me on the shoulder and said,

"Cyndi, your shoes are nice and all, but are they that nice?"

I looked up, likely for the first time since I had been in class, at this warm smile and concerned eyes. Willard and I became lifelong buddies, and we took every class offered at Agape together for the next four years.

By that summer, I was hooked on taking classes but to my chagrin, none were offered for a few months. During service, I heard the announcer mention the 'New Members Class' – a complimentary 10-week series – would be starting soon and I signed up. One of the great things that occurred during those classes was that Rev. Michael would stop by to say a few words. The day he stopped by, he stood in front of me, placed his thumb on my forehead, and said,

"You are going to be a Practitioner."

Great, but what's a practitioner? I thought.

That same summer I had a dream...

August 1, 2011:

I was in Rev. Michael's house, sleeping. When I finally woke up, I got the feeling he understood just how tired I was and my need for rest. As I slept, he kept watch over me and allowed me to rest. When I sat up, we began talking.

"You know, being vegetarian would be a good choice for you," Rev. Michael said.

The dream continued and I had woken up from yet another nap and Rev. Michael still stood over me. He handed me a couple of crisp, dark green and brown bills. They weren't anything like the money we use currently. The bills had an eco-friendly energy.

"Here this will make you feel better," he said.

I'm grateful but money isn't what makes my soul happy, I thought as I took the bills in my hand. I then woke up from another nap and my next guest was Felicia Rashad. Does she know the Beckwiths? I wondered. I used to watch her on The Cosby Show as I was growing up and to me, she represented the image of a nurturing, intelligent, and strong mother and woman. Seeing her in my dream felt very comforting. She seemed like the kind of mother who only wanted the best for her children, and I had always longed for that.

I then woke up from another nap and sitting at my bedside was Rickie Byars. I sat up as we talked and laughed.

"I need you in our choir," she said. I chuckled then responded,

"But I CAN'T sing!" I jumped out of bed and felt rested.

"I need to do my part around here," I said.

I noticed a vacuum and began to clean. As I vacuumed, I looked out the window and noticed the building and lush lawn outside. Rev. Michael walked over and said,

"Come on, let's go check it out" and then he took me on a tour of the grounds.

There were classrooms and a sanctuary, and the entire building was buzzing with activity. There were children in the different classrooms. Some studied ballet, while others created pieces of art. Then I woke up.

Those who know me know that I love interpreting my dreams and I was able to come up with a translation that felt good to me. The choir symbolized strength and power in numbers and that I am never alone. The choir also was a symbol of spiritual fortitude and religious fervor. Felicia Rashad represented mother energy and in general, dreams of a mother or of your mother are about unconditional love, spirit, life, protection, and nurturing. Money symbolized energy, power, and resources and that success and prosperity were within my reach. And lastly, the reference to being a vegetarian indicated that I was paying close attention to the energy I was taking in and ingesting. I was in touch with my natural drives and instincts and was taking responsibility for the care of my animal instincts and of those who needed my care.

I enjoyed attending services, taking classes, and growing at Agape. I didn't quite understand everything Rev. Michael said, but his words felt good to my soul.

Is it possible that I am as wonderful as he says we are?

I had been dealing with the autoimmune condition for some time when I arrived at Agape. During one of his services, Rev. Michael spoke about the process the caterpillar goes through as it becomes a butterfly.

What if I stepped into my own cocoon and allowed my imaginal cells to recreate themselves? Could I be healed?

I was willing to find out. A couple of months after my dream, I met Rev. Cheryl Ward, one of the ministers at Agape, in a class. I realized she was the woman in my dream, not Felicia Rashad, which made me feel our relationship had been destined.

Chapter 19
In Service to Love

I was ready to increase my service at Agape as it had started to feel more and more like my spiritual home, but I didn't know the best way to be of service. That same August, I met a sweet soul at Agape who told me about the Registration Ministry. She introduced me to the Dean of Registration and then I was off to attend Adrianne and Alfred's (two of my best friends) wedding in Maui. While in Maui, I saw a string of emails going back and forth. Alice Beckwith, the mother of Rev. Michael Bernard Beckwith, was upset because students wanted to register for classes, but no one was present at the registration table. I decided in that moment that I would officially volunteer to serve on the registration team upon my return.

This opportunity felt like it was created by God and was perfect for me in numerous ways. First, it allowed me to interact with people. I was beginning to set my shyness aside and was learning how to show up even when my shyness was fully present. Second, it gave me a sense of belonging I hadn't previously felt. Third, that commitment kept me coming back to Agape week after week, even when I wanted to sleep in on a Sunday morning. I knew someone would need to register for class and so it got me up and out of bed each week.

Because of the amazing transformation I was experiencing through attending those classes, I was excited to somehow play a small role in someone else's transformation. I don't think a single Sunday went by the first year when I didn't serve at the table. Had it not been for this commitment, which took place in response to Alice Beckwith being upset, I would not have been tethered long enough for God to go to work on me. This kept me at Agape when my usual pattern was one of initial fascination and then losing interest.

One day as I stood outside at the registration table, I looked up to the sky and said,

"God, I really like it here. If you want me to have a partner, can you bring him here and put a sign over his head that says, 'This is him' so I know who he is because I never want to leave here."

As service let out and the crowds poured into the parking lot, a young man stopped by and whispered in my ear,

"You look beautiful in your white dress," and kept walking.

I looked up at the sky and silently said,

"God, I didn't mean I was ready right now!"

The young man was Jesse. I had met him in a class I was enrolled in with Rev. Michael and Rev. Cheryl. The first time I noticed Jesse in class I thought, *he's cute but stay away from him, he is in his healing process.* Plus, he wasn't my type. He had long hair and tattoos and I was into clean-cut, business types.

One day after class, Jesse approached me and said he was aware I could assist him with filing his divorce papers and wanted to know if I could help him. I told him that I would.

As we continued to move through classes, it became apparent we were beginning to like one another. We spent long hours talking on the phone. He loved Wayne Dyer, I loved Wayne Dyer. We both loved Rev. Michael and Agape. We moved through a couple of classes together and began to talk about setting up a date (by this point, it was March 2012).

We decided that we would go on our first date after service on a Sunday. However, we received the news that the church would be holding a memorial service for Alice Beckwith immediately after service. Jesse and I both looked at each other and decided we wanted to stay. It was because of Alice that I was serving at the registration table the day that I told God I was ready for my beloved and then Jesse showed up. Her memorial service was a thing of beauty and really honored the woman Alice was.

Afterward, Jesse and I went on our first official date for dinner at a Mexican restaurant in downtown L.A. The conversation was engaging, and I enjoyed learning more about him; I could tell he enjoyed listening to and learning more about me, too. As we walked to the car after dinner, I said to Jesse,

"I'm open to going out again if you like."

He took a moment before responding.

"I like you; I just want to date you," he said. I was a bit puzzled and asked,

"You mean you want to get to know one another within a relationship?"

When he agreed, I immediately thought a potential relationship could be disastrous. We set up some ground rules with the most important one being that if our relationship didn't work out, neither of us would leave Agape. It was our one non-negotiable and we both agreed to it.

We attempted to keep our relationship private but our affection for one another grew daily. While in the Self

Awareness Class with Rev. Cheryl one day, she saw us sitting next to each other holding hands when she came over and asked,

"Do I need to bless this?"

We both nodded in agreement. I thought her blessing meant that things would be smooth sailing between Jesse and me, but that wasn't the case at all. Her blessing placed us in a container of divine grace; Jesse and I were about to embark on the most intense healing we had ever experienced within our relationship.

I was so wounded because of life experiences that I constantly sought to protect myself. I could not believe that his love was true and so I would break up with him almost weekly. At one point, Jesse stood his ground and refused to accept my apology. He cut off all communication with me. I could not reach him via phone, email, or in person. I began to realize my way of being was not normal, healthy, or loving.

One of the things that I admired about Jesse was his ability to love so easily and that was something I wanted to cultivate within myself. This was not going to occur unless I started to release the feelings of unworthiness, which proved to be one of the hardest things I would ever have to do.

The first three years of our relationship were the hardest. We had ups and downs and through it all, we both had to make conscious choices to heal our wounds as this was the only way to be able to remain in the relationship. What I came to realize was that for so long I wanted a partner to love and who loved me, but relationships are not for the ego's purpose. Relationships are an accelerated classroom. Triggers are easily accessible and inevitably get pushed, not because the individuals are 'bad' people, but because the relationship is the container in which both beings are held in to heal. If one is courageous enough and doesn't run, eventually you reach a level of healing where the relationship becomes the foundation upon which two whole beings stand as they go about being a beneficial presence on the planet.

Jesse and I married in February 2022, and it was the most beautiful and sacred ceremony. It was facilitated by Rev. Michael, Dr. Sue Morter, Akili Beckwith, and Rev. Cheryl Ward. All our teachers walked us home. To top it off, my son walked me down the aisle and Jesse's daughters walked him.

Jesse's vows affirmed me as the strength he didn't know he needed and the joy he didn't know he lacked. Mine spoke to the courage he had demonstrated by stand ing by my side when I was ill and sometimes a little crazy and how he was and is my biggest cheerleader.

I love that he loves to explore this planet with me and allows and encourages me to be my authentic self.

Chapter 20
The Practitioner's Way

P ractitioner sessions are spiritual counseling sessions that begin and end with prayer. Additionally, the counselor works with spiritual principles and holds an unwavering knowing about the individual and the situation.

Here is a more formal description of what a practitioner is within the context of Agape:

> "A practitioner is not merely a body of knowledge, but rather a state of consciousness that realizes oneness with the Infinite. Dedicated to first demonstrating New Thought/Ageless Wisdom principles within his/her own life, a practitioner then serves as a spiritually therapeutic agent of the Spirit for the upliftment of every man, woman, and child who requests healing of body, mind, and spirit."

One of the things Rev. Michael advised over the years regarding relationships was to not share our relationship issues with friends and family as it's challenging for them to remain neutral. The best thing one can do is take the issue to a practitioner so he can assist him or her in seeing the Truth about the situation, herself, and her beloved.

I remembered that when the time came in my relationship with Jesse. Anytime things got heated with Jesse, I scheduled a session with my spiritual therapist, Akili, and told him everything that was happening. I was able to do this because a practitioner holds everything in the utmost confidence.

How often have you felt safe to express without holding back because you knew you were safe?

This was a whole new experience for me.

As I progressed in my healing, I was able to access more patience with myself and others. In the past, I was quick to end things because of my anger and fear. I was learning how to pause, bracket what was happening, and take it to my practitioner. Once I met with my practitioner and came to my senses, then it was safe to continue the conversation with Jesse.

We diligently looked at everything that came up from a place of non-judgment and self-forgiveness. This allowed me to stand before Jesse healed and whole. I no longer needed to run and hide my wounds. Of course, this took some time, but the day Akili walked into the practitioner's room where they held vigil for service and saw Jesse and me sitting together, he said,

"That's a lot of answered prayer right there."

Throughout my years of study at Agape, I had met with a handful of practitioners for assistance with various issues. The one area I didn't allow myself to have hope in was my health. Since a man in a white coat told me my condition was lifelong, I took what he said at face value. Thankfully, something had begun to shift. During my first year of practitioner studies, I decided I would let Rev. Kathleen McNamara, a minister of Agape, in on the condition I had been dealing with since 2002. During our session, Rev. Kathleen asked me,

"On a scale of 1 to 10, how much do you believe you can be healed?"

I responded, "I am at a 2."

The look on her face was one of surprise but I continued,

"That's why I am here to see you because I am not able to know it for myself and so I need you to know it for me."

After our session, I did as she taught. I released the beautiful prayer she had spoken and simply sat with the knowing that at some point I'd return to wholeness and in the meantime, I had work to do.

Whenever someone asks me about practitioner studies, the first thing I tell them is,

"It's the best thing I ever did for myself."

Practitioner studies helped me address and begin to heal the years of trauma I had lived through. As you know by reading my story, life had not been easy and up until this point, the focus had been on surviving, and through practitioner studies, I was given the tools to heal. Those two years were a commitment to me, and that commitment meant,

"I love myself enough to do this work, no matter how hard it gets."

At the time, I desperately attempted to cultivate self-love, but I kept running into roadblocks.

In addition to healing practices, we were also learning Agape's six steps of affirmative prayer. I couldn't seem to get past the third step of the process, which required the person praying to unify his/herself with God. I didn't believe I was one with God then. I knew everyone else was and I envied them for it. Somehow, I thought I was the exception.

As I tried to learn how to pray in this way, it dawned on me to call a practitioner for help. After our session, I went out to the living room, sat on the couch, and began to pray according to the steps, when I heard trumpets blow. I opened my eyes, looked around the room, and no one was there. Then I heard,

"We are blowing the trumpets because God is in the room."

Where? I thought. Then the voice said,

"It's here as you."

The trumpets blared again. I then realized that I was not outside nor separate from God and simultaneously, this awareness was reframed by past experiences when I thought I was alone.

By the end of practitioner studies, my class had elected me to respond to The Charge. I was to speak on behalf of our graduating class and affirm our commitment as practitioners. I was still very shy, so I went to see a practitioner help me with stepping up to take on this task. The session was facilitated by Rev. Carlton Teabout and during our session, I had the shift that allowed me to view my election as a soulful recognition. The Charge was an opportunity to acknowledge what my classmates and I had walked through. It was a chance to release what was not true about who we thou

ght we were and embrace what has always been. From this place, I was able to let Spirit flow through me that day. During our initiation ceremony with Rev. Michael, he bestowed a God quality as my essence, and it was Grace. If nothing else, the one thing I had been aware of through my often-turbulent life, was that Grace had been present and so it seemed more than appropriate this was to be my quality.

Chapter 21
To Minister or Not to Minister?

My life was in bloom, and I was in a good space within myself. I was a faithful Agape member and had immersed myself in the culture. Things were abuzz at Agape as the leadership team was preparing to relaunch the ministerial school. While so many people were excited about the changes and the possibility of enrolling, I was in deep dialogue with God.

"I am doing well, am I not?" I asked.

"I am a spiritual therapist. I assist in facilitating classes at Agape. Do I really need to go to ministerial school?"

It was Jesse's birthday weekend, and we planned on taking a road trip that would begin in Sedona and end in Las Vegas. Two of our favorite musicians were performing at one of the hotels, and it would be the perfect way to celebrate his birthday.

As we approached Sedona, we saw a big storm moving in. Although I didn't say anything to Jesse, I was going through an internal storm of my own. The following day, Jess and I went on a hike to Cathedral Rock. I'd been there several times but somehow, I got us lost. What should have been a three-hour hike turned into a six-hour ordeal. The entire time, I argued with God in my mind.

"Am I not doing enough? Why do I have to go to ministerial school? I don't want to live in a fishbowl! I don't want to live a life of transparency."

I am not one to argue with God, but in that moment, I was experiencing a lot of resistance. My feelings and the level of them felt 10 times bigger than the storm that was about to drench Sedona. Luckily, we found our way off the mountain just in time.

That night I had a dream and in it, Rev. Michael appeared and said,

"As you walk, you will heal."

What do you mean? Have I not been walking my walk? Why do I have to go beyond this? I thought.

The following day, my hip went out. Did it go out because I overworked it during the six-hour hike? Did it have something to do with what Rev. Michael said in the dream? I gathered my strength and limped it off. Jess and I left for Las Vegas and went on to enjoy the rest of this birthday trip.

Upon our return to Los Angeles, I surrendered my white flag and completed the ministerial school application. I submitted it but not before limping around for three days. Not surprisingly, my hip went back into place shortly after I submitted my application. We all have a destiny and purpose; mine had something to do with ministry.

Ministerial studies were about to facilitate healing for me on a whole new level.

Although I had the vision of myself on a pulpit in 1993, I never wanted to be a public speaker. In fact, every time I had to share in class, I would sweat profusely because I would get so nervous.

How was I supposed to do something that required me to speak publicly all the time?

In the beginning, I would get so nervous while attempting to deliver a talk that I was certain I was going to flunk out of ministerial school. The interesting thing was that not trying was a fate worse than death, so I just kept going.

One day as I sat in class, I looked out the window and the sun was beginning to set. In that moment, I flashed back to my visit with a psychic in Sedona in 2007. During this trip, she said,

"You often see red flags and tend to ignore them."

She was referring to how my relationships with men had been up until that point. She went on to tell me that this behavior would begin to shift for me. She assured me that I would go from 20 red flags to 10 to 5 down to eventually one flag to know when someone was not for me. She also asked me if I had read the book '*Jonathan Livingston Seagull*' and proceeded to tell me the gist of it. Jonathan was a seagull who longed to fly and see what was beyond the mountains. Each time he went to fly, his friends would throw things at him, which forced him to back down.

"The friends that surround you now are like the seagulls who didn't want Jonathan to fly," she said.

"There is a flock of seagulls you belong to, and they are waiting for you."

That evening in ministerial class, I turned around and looked at my classmates. Many of the individuals were people I had spent the past eight years with, and they were my flock. I had found my tribe. I spent the next four years with these individuals and for the first time in my life shared my story during one of my talks.

As time went by, I continued delivering talks despite the nerves I felt. I remembered what I heard that fateful day on the radio in 1993 as God spoke to Moses and said,

"When the time comes, it will be I who does the talking through you."

Chapter 22
The Energy Codes

In 2016, our ministerial studies program brought Dr. Sue Morter to teach a two-day class on The Energy Codes. I had heard Dr. Sue speak at Agape a few times and had always enjoyed her talks. Much like my first-time visiting Agape, the concepts Dr. Sue spoke about during her workshop were not necessarily things I was familiar with, and yet everything she said resonated. At the end of the workshop, Dr. Sue offered my classmates and me her upcoming Level 1 at a fraction of the cost. I was so intrigued by the workshop that I signed Jesse and me up.

The Energy Codes are a set of practices you can do to generate your own quantum flip – to take yourself from confusion, lack, and dis-ease, to clarity, being in the flow, and wellness. These practices help you to build circuits that support your true nature as an energy being. They also assist you in shifting from living from the protective personality (i.e. fight or flight) to living creatively from the level of Soul/Higher Self. These practices and teachings assist an individual in getting under a painful and/or difficult story to address it at the level of energy.

Energy Codes Level II

While attending Dr. Sue's Level II in Cancun in 2018, I had a series of mystical dreams, but one stood out. One of the things I had difficulty with throughout my life was speaking up. As a child, I was often the recipient of an unexpected slap across the face for interjecting myself into adult conversations. At 15 years old, I entered a relationship with a young man that would further suppress my voice and spirit. And there I was at 47 years old, unknowingly about to embark on a journey of unblocking that energy.

May 2018:

> A young Asian girl appeared with an older gentleman who pulled the cart she sat on. She was very friendly, and we began to engage in a conversation when my ex-husband appeared and said,
>
> "You can't speak to her."

I was infuriated! It took every bit of energy and courage I could gather to say,

"You can't tell me who I can and who I cannot speak to anymore!"

And just like that, he was gone. I knew this was a dream, but it didn't change the fact that I was incredibly proud of myself for having the courage to speak up. As I returned my attention to my newfound friend, she said

"I have a secret to share with you." I said,

"Go ahead, you can trust me."

She proceeded to place her hand in her pants and pulled out what appeared to be a penis. Turned out she was born with both female and male organs. I was so honored she entrusted me with such a personal secret.

(End of dream)

That morning as we gathered in the ballroom for our coursework, I shared the dream with Dr. Sue and what my interpretation of it was. I felt I had an energetic shift in my chakra system, specifically with the second and fifth chakras. Dr. Sue nodded in agreement and added,

"That's what Spirit is up to. It is merging the masculine and feminine as we return to Oneness."

Her words washed over me like a cosmic shower of knowledge and on a deep level, I knew those words were true. I felt incredibly blessed that the Universe entrusted me with such information.

Jesse and I returned home from an incredible experience with Dr. Sue and our spiritual cups were full. We had timed our return with my monthly infusion of immune globulin. The nurse arrived at my home, and she hooked me up to the I.V. I climbed into bed and prepared to watch television for a bit. These treatments were something I looked forward to because they gave me permission to disconnect from the world and relax twice a month. I usually scheduled my treatments for Sunday and Monday evenings so it would not interfere with my work schedule.

During my treatment, I felt a pain shoot through the center of my chest almost instantly. It felt about the size of a quarter at first, and it was hard to breathe. The area of pain grew and spread throughout my chest. I yelled out for the nurse and told her I thought I was having a heart attack. My nurse had been with me since 2007, and this had never happened before.

"If you are having a heart attack, your left arm would hurt," she said.

I freaked out and yelled,

"My arm does hurt!"

"That's your right arm," she responded.

I breathed deeply and after about 15 minutes, the pain subsided. The nurse asked if I wanted to go to the emergency room, and I told her no. I remembered that I had just returned from a healing retreat, and I had some profound experiences there that had to do with my heart chakra.

Maybe this is what it feels like to have my heart open?

The next day, I decided to research the medication to see if it had any side effects. Never in the 14 years of receiving those treatments had it dawned on me to see if it had any side effects (I was just thankful to have regained my mobility.). I discovered that physicians were aware intravenous immunoglobulin could cause a stroke or heart attack. I was so frightened by the experience that I stopped using the medication immediately. I then researched a more natural approach and consulted a naturopathic doctor.

Chapter 23
Welcoming and
Surrendering to H.E.L.P

N ear the end of June 2018, Jesse and I prepared to travel to El Salvador for my son's wedding. It was to be a three-day event, complete with all the bells, whistles, activities, and glamour. Since I had been off the medicine, I went to see the naturopathic doctor and asked if there was something extra she could give me. When we arrived in El Salvador, everything moved quickly. The festivities began with a welcome dinner on Friday night, then hair and make-up early Saturday followed by a beautiful church ceremony, and an all-out extravaganza of a reception. On Sunday morning, we drove to my new daughter in love's family beach home.

I always loved swimming, especially in the ocean, so I didn't think twice about running in when we arrived at the beach house. Unbeknownst to me, El Salvador is a surfing mecca due to its swells. Surfers come from near and far to enjoy her monstrous waves, but I wasn't paying attention. As soon as I got in the ocean, I could feel the rocks hitting my rib cage. They were coming from every direction! I realized this was not an ordinary ocean and when I went to swim back to shore, I realized I had no strength in my limbs. I had been off the neuropathy medication for almost two months, and I had grown very weak. I began to go under the water.

I looked over at Jesse, who was also getting beat up by the rocks and the waves, and I signaled for us to head in. I looked up and noticed my son was watching us from the balcony.

"Please don't let me die here," I said to God. "It's their wedding weekend!"

In that moment, I remembered a story Rev. Michael had shared about his recent beach experience in Costa Rica. He had been taken out quickly by the ocean's current and realized that the harder he swam, the less progress he made. As his daughter stood at the shore worried about him, he turned up and said,

"HELP. I need help!"

All of this occurred to me in a flash, and I silently yelled out,

"H.E.L.P!" which stands for Hello Eternal Loving Presence.

I turned over on my back, took in a deep breath, and swam as hard as I could. Intellectually, I knew I didn't have the strength needed to make it in, but I was not about to be bound by logic. Within a few moments, I was on the shore being pushed onto the rocks by the crashing waves. I had never been so glad to feel a hard surface against my skin. Jesse rushed over and tried to get me to stand, but my legs felt like jelly. My son ran towards me, concerned, and asked,

"Are you OK, Mom?"

For the first time in my life, I said,

"No, no I am not OK."

Up until that point, I had 'toughed' my way through life and kept the effects of my health challenges mostly to myself.

I was done pretending to be OK and playing strong. I was done trying so hard to hide from everyone.

Since I was off the Immune Globulin medication, I quickly lost mobility, which meant I had to open up to allowing someone else to care for me. My partner, Jesse, stepped in without hesitation and did so

beautifully. This, too, was a deep healing for me. I went from having felt alone most of my life and having to do everything on my own to feeling safe enough in my relationship that I could surrender to such a degree. I became like a defenseless child who needed someone to dress me, comb my hair, cook my meals, and drive me to and from doctor's appointments. I always knew Jesse had a good heart, but I never imagined I'd need to lean on him in that way.

If you ask people about my personality, one of the first things they will likely say is that I am always smiling and am an optimistic person overall.

Was this in fact who I was or was it the version of me I had shown the world for so long, all the while internally screaming in quiet desperation?

I felt the fight was beginning to wear on me and at a certain point, I simply couldn't pretend anymore. At one point, I began looking at wheelchairs in anticipation of what was to come as I was having a hard time just getting from the front door to the elevator. I remember Jesse walked into the room as I was looking at the wheelchair options and he turned to me and said,

"That's it? You're just going to give up?"

His determination and belief in me and God would need to carry us both because I just didn't have it in me.

The following day, I reached out to a group of friends from Agape and asked if they could support me in prayer. Up until then, they didn't know that I dealt with medical issues. I continued to surrender and learned how to ask for assistance, and I learned to never underestimate the power of prayer. I had some of the most spiritually steeped practitioners and ministers praying and affirming the truth about my being.

Jesse and I established a routine. Before leaving for his eight-hour work shift, he ensured that I was fed, bathed, and dressed. Since I was unable to move around much, I'd sit on the couch and read, pray, and meditate while he was gone. One day, it occurred to me that it was time to have a conversation with God.

"OK, God, you have my undivided attention," I said.

"Is there something you'd like me to know?"

After a few moments, I continued,

"If there is nothing else I get out of this experience, may I finally realize my oneness with you?"

I had often heard that life speaks in whispers, but when we don't listen, it begins to yell. Life was yelling at me and finally, I was listening.

"What was God trying to tell me?"

I was determined to find out. I realized that as exciting as life had been, it was about to get even better. I was about to embark on a journey that would change the trajectory of my life under the guise of a 'health condition'.

Chapter 24
Everything is Energy

I n the fall of 2018, after traveling to Indiana and completing Level III of the Energy Codes Course, I had a Spiritual B.E.S.T. session with Dr. Sue. She recommended I begin working with a local Spiritual B.E.S.T. Practitioner when I returned home to Los Angeles and that was exactly what I did.

According to Dr. Sue, B.E.S.T., or Bio-Energetic Synchronization Technique, is a non-forceful, energy balancing, the hands-on procedure used to help reestablish the full healing potential of the body. B.E.S.T. is widely used by health care practitioners all over the world who practice mind/body healing and recognize that the body is more than the sum of its parts. It is a system of health care that is state of the art in balancing body, mind, memory, and spirit energy fields, and enhancing the flow of that energy throughout the entire system. It is a whole-body healing technique.

> Bio-Energetic Synchronization Technique is a non-invasive technique to remove interference from the body, allowing the body to re-establish and maintain full healing potential. It addresses the cause as opposed to symptoms by focusing on the person as a whole being (physical, mental, emotional, and spiritual aspects). ~ Dr. Sue Morter

The B.E.S.T. practice had become a part of my healing regimen, along with the Agape Practitioner Counseling Sessions, my daily spiritual practice, and everything else I was doing. I noticed major differences in the way I processed life experiences. One big difference was that I stopped reacting. A peace and awareness washed over me, and from that space, I was able to feel into and communicate what was coming up for me at the moment. I also noticed an ease by which things flowed in my life. I no longer had to effort or make things happen. Life was meeting me where I was, and grace was present.

As life always does, it gave me plenty of opportunities to see if I had learned the lessons in releasing my old ways of being.

In 2020, while attending a training with Dr. Sue online, I had a total meltdown. Three of my biggest fears had risen from my subconscious and onto the screen of life…

1. **Being audited by the IRS.** Since I was viewed as an entity, I always filed my taxes early. Over the years, I had created an S-Corp for my counseling practice and wanted to expand it into sacred travel. The IRS decided to audit me for the previous four years and I was beside myself; when I contacted my accountant, she would not return any of my calls. Fear No. 1.

2. **Losing my medical insurance.** At the time, Jesse and I were frequently visiting Las Vegas to look for a home to purchase. During one of those trips, Jesse received a call from his job. They were terminating his employment and informed him that his insurance benefits would end in 30 days. Jesse's job had graciously agreed to cover me when I stopped working at the law firm in 2018 and with that news, I didn't know what to do. The IVIG infusions cost $30k per month. Fear No. 2.

3. **Being homeless.** Because of my unstable childhood, I had a long-standing fear of being without a home. Jesse and I had found a house, entered escrow, and everything

appeared to be moving along smoothly. Just before we were to close escrow, a forgotten-about bill I deferred during COVID-19 popped up on my credit report, which placed me over the allowed debt-to-income ratio. It shut the entire loan process down. We had already given notice at our apartment in Huntington Beach and were essentially about to be homeless. Fear No. 3.

Earlier that day, I had cried in the shower and did my best to not let Jesse hear me. My way of being in the world was to be in charge and able to handle everything that came my way. When Jesse left the hotel room so that I could attend the training with Dr. Sue, I lost it. I didn't have it in me to play strong any longer and I needed help. I explained to her that I had been doing central channel breathing throughout everything, but I was in total overwhelm. To have shared this with her and my fellow classmates was quite a leap for me. Allowing myself to be vulnerable in a public setting was healing in and of itself.

Note: Central channel breathing is a foundational technique in breathwork. In essence, you inhale the breath from two feet above the crown into your heart or belly, then exhale the breath into the Earth.

Dr. Sue heard me and held me, and I felt the love coming from the entire class. She agreed to speak with me the following week. During that conversation, something Dr. Sue said had a profound effect on me. She said,

"You do realize you don't have to grow through pain and trauma anymore, don't you?"

Her statement flooded my awareness with so much clarity; it was a completely brand-new way of being for me. I didn't realize there was another way to grow other than through pain and trauma. It was as if someone turned on the light.

The next day, Jesse and I decided to view some apartments in Las Vegas. We figured we had already given notice at our apartment, he was no longer employed at his company, so perhaps this clean start was just what we needed. Immediately, we found a beautiful, three-bedroom apartment in a quiet part of Las Vegas. It had a washer and dryer in the unit which was a luxury we had not had before, and it cost $1000 less per month than our apartment in California. One of the reasons we had decided to relocate in the first place was because the cost of living was too high in California, and I was bringing in less money since I stopped working at the law firm. Little did we know at the time that we decided to make the move that Jesse would be released from his job, and I was beginning to see God's handiwork taking shape. The idea to even consider relocating was feeling God-inspired.

Once we were moved into our new apartment, I sat back on the couch, took a deep breath, and said,

"God, if I am to lose mobility due to not having my monthly treatments, for now, I just want to thank you for the roof overhead and my loving partner who takes such good care of me. I know you are here with me."

Later that week, Dr. Sue connected me with a local Spiritual B.E.S.T. Practitioner in Henderson, NV. Dr. Lorri Mandekic and I began working together in March 2021. When I walked into her office, I shared with her all that was happening in my life.

Fast forward to now and I am a completely different person. The deep-seated fear that resided in my belly is gone. The fear and hesitancy I had to enjoy public speaking is gone. I have begun teaching classes on the Energy Codes and even taught my first class at Agape and I have never felt more grounded, centered, and in my body as I do today.

Granted, prior to working with Dr. Lorri, I worked with Gina DeMasi in Los Angeles for two years who is also a Spiritual B.E.S.T. Practitioner. Dr. Lorri says Gina did all the heavy lifting and that she was brought in for the easy/fun part. What I can tell you is that when I first began working with Gina in 2018, I was in dire shape physically and was unaware of how much I was holding subconsciously.

After working with both Dr. Lorri and Gina, The Energy Codes, Spirt, and embodying my Higher Self, I feel so incredibly alive. I trust life is for me and constantly providing me with opportunities to discover more of who I came here to be.

Because of my three biggest fears happening simultaneously in 2021, I now walk as a sovereign being. There is not a whole lot left that frightens me or knocks me off my center. I can remain grounded during challenges and to a degree feel a sense of excitement. I liken it to seeing a tornado approaching and making myself comfortable at its center.

Chapter 25
Sacred Travel

Healing isn't linear, and neither are the ways I have healed and continue to heal. Sacred travel is one of those non-linear ways of healing that has been such an amazing part of my journey. Travel has allowed me to experience the beauty and diversity of our planet. Through travel, I have been exposed to the healing energies available in various locations that assisted me not only in healing physically, but mentally, emotionally, and spiritually. I believe Mother Earth is here to assist us in our awakening and finding a way to allow her to support me has been a healing in and of itself. The following destinations have contributed greatly to my healing journey…

Egypt

Originally, I wanted to go to Egypt in 2004 but I was faced with a dilemma. I had to decide whether to use the money to go to Egypt or  use it to move out and leave my marriage. I chose the latter. Sedona Soul Adventures alternated sacred journeys between Egypt, Peru, and Bali, and when Egypt came around again in 2007, I went. As luck would have it, I was able to borrow from my 401k and paid myself back gradually. Like so many people, I grew up seeing images of Egypt in TV documentaries. When I arrived in Egypt, I could not believe my eyes. I was standing next to and inside of the megalithic structures that previously had only been available to me through TV. The air was electric and dreamlike. I tried to be as present as possible; I lamented the thought of even missing one single moment.

There is something potent about Egypt and I don't think people end up there by chance. Egypt is where individuals have traveled throughout millennia to study in her mystery schools and go through various levels of initiations. Our group was no exception.

As I reflect on my first visit to the pyramids and temples, I am aware that I was cracked open each time I visited and prepared for the next phase of my expansion.

Recently, I came across two books *'Anna, The Grandmother of Jesus'* and *'Anna, The Voice of the Magdalene's'* by Claire Heartsong. Both books discuss the origins of the Essene Community and the Magdalene Order that Jesus (Yeshua), his mother Mary, his grandmother Anna, and Mary of Magdalene belonged to. The books speak to the teachings originating in the mystery schools of Egypt and the School of Isis. Many of the Magdalene and Essenes traveled from Carmel to Egypt in preparation for their role in the Christ drama. Yeshua spent time in the pyramids and underwent his own preparation, study, and initiations. When I think about the fact that I stood within the same Great Pyramid where Yeshua and Mary of Magdalene spent time, my entire body becomes covered in goosebumps. Is it any wonder that I was drawn to this magical place known as Egypt and have returned four times since my first visit? Each time I return, I feel I am blessed with an internal upgrade that prepares me on every level for the next stage of my unfoldment.

Sedona

I returned to Sedona in 2008 for a weekend workshop with Shaman Jose Luis Delgado from Peru. As I stood in the hallway waiting for the workshop to begin, the shaman approached me. He looked me in the eyes and said,

"Your problem is that you don't live in your heart."

I didn't know who this man was, and he didn't even know me.

What does he know of my heart?

I was taken aback by this very perceptive comment coming from a stranger but as life would have it, he was right.

All the trauma I had experienced over the years had shielded me from living from my heart and if I was honest with myself, I had no idea how to live from my heart. There was a big difference between being a 'good' person and constantly ignoring one's intuition for the sake of 'others', which was the space I had lived from. I learned early on to operate from the level of mind. If there was something to be figured out, it was to be done with thought and data that I acquired. I'd heard it said that the longest 18 inches one travels is from the head into the heart. Don Delgado had done his job. He planted a seed that would light the path from my head into my heart. Although I was a 'good' person, I struggled with self-love, and he and I both knew it.

Fatima, Portugal

During the winter of 2019, I had the opportunity to travel to the Sanctuary of Our

Lady of Fatima, a beautiful cathedral known for its miracles. The story of this sacred site began in the village of Fatima, Portugal, on May 13, 1917. On that day near the tiny village of the Virgin Mary, three young children  appeared: Francisco (age 10), Jacinta (age 9), and Lucia (age 7). As was the custom, the children were tending their family's sheep when a lady dressed in all white, luminescent, and indescribably beautiful appeared. From May through October 1917, the Lady appeared and spoke to the children on the 13th day of each month. News of these apparitions began to spread. The children recounted that the Virgin told them that God had sent her with a message for every man, woman, and child living in the century. She promised that God would grant peace to the entire world if her requests for prayer, reparation, and consecration were heard and obeyed.

Over the years, hundreds of thousands of people visited this site for miracles, and I was no exception. Some shuffled on their knees and prayed the Rosary. Others prayed aloud while traversing the mega-huge, park-lined esplanade.

Although I was not a practicing Catholic, I believed in God with all my heart and soul, and sacred sites spoke to me. (Maybe it was because such places were saturated in prayer that simply being in its energy felt good to the soul.) I was not too proud to ask for a miracle as I, too, needed a healing. I did not walk across the concourse on my knees; instead, I picked out a candle shaped in the form of the human body, said a prayer, and threw it into the massive fire that burned outside the cathedral. The fire was where everyone placed their prayers, releasing them to Spirit.

As I flew home after my time in Portugal, I prayed to God and said,

"If it is your will that I return to work at the law firm, I will do it. I only ask that you provide me with a body that can do the work."

I also told God I no longer wished to live in fear and would face life heart on, turning away from nothing.

The following morning, my cell phone rang. I could tell the call was from the claim representative that had been investigating my disability claim for the past several months. Our calls were never pleasant as I felt they didn't believe I was ill. So, instead of my usual apprehension to take the call, I picked up while simultaneously saying to myself,

"I will not be afraid anymore."

The voice on the other end wasted no time in telling me, that after conducting a thorough investigation of my claim and compiling all the medical records from all my doctors, they had determined I was indeed 'disabled.' She was calling to let me know how much I would receive monthly until I turned 67 years old. For the first time in my life, I would have the time and space to see what it meant to simply be. I would be able to focus on healing.

God heard my prayer, and I received my miracle.

Chapter 26
Plant Medicine and the Toads

M y healing journey naturally directed me onto a path of working with certain plant medicines. I experienced and worked with quite a few over the years. Below are a few that I worked with and the story behind how each one found me.

BUFO

As I sat on the couch one day, I turned the TV to my favorite spiritual channel, Gaia. In one of their series, they introduced a doctor on the show, Octavio Rettig. He lived in Hermosillo, Sonora Mexico. Octavio had studied western medicine in Guadalajara and somewhere along the way, became addicted to crack cocaine. One day, a friend of his gave him a substance that contained the venom from the Sonoran Toad, known as Bufo Alvarius. After smoking the substance, Octavio called his friend and said,

"You just saved my life."

Octavio had such a profound spiritual experience that he was able to stop using crack cocaine on the spot. Octavio gave up his medical practice, began studying with the shaman from the local Seri tribe, and has dedicated his life to assisting individuals heal through the 'toad medicine.'

I wondered if my previous drug use was something that affected my constitution. I found Octavio on social media and sent him a message. I didn't expect to hear back from him and was surprised when he responded within minutes. I explained my history and health condition to him, and he said,

"I am at your service Cynthia."

Just like that, contact was made, and I was off to research this psychedelic known as Bufo. I had never heard of this type of medicine before, and I found it strange that people smoked the secretion of a frog in a glass pipe. Eventually, I came upon a show called *Hamilton's Pharmacopeia*. In this episode, the scientist, Hamilton, traveled to the Sonoran Desert to study and experience Bufo Alvarious. The shaman who administered the medicine was Dr. Gerry Sandoval. Since I had tried to schedule an appointment with Octavio but with no response, I reached out to Dr.

Gerry. Within minutes, we confirmed our appointment with him. We were heading to San Luis Rio Colorado, Mexico.

On the surface, everything looked like it happened by chance, but when you dig deeper, you can see the hand of God in it.

I had been estranged from my father for 23 years and about two years earlier, my dad found me via social media. We had spoken here and there, and he often asked when I would come to see him. To get to Dr. Gerry, we would have to drive through the town my father lived in. *Coincidence?* Jesse and I decided we would drive into Puerto Penasco first where Dr. Gerry lived, and then stop and see my dad on our way home. I was incredibly nervous, but I had done my due diligence and felt good; the person who administered the medicine was also trained in western medicine.

On the day of the ceremony, Dr. Gerry and his assistant prayed me in:

> *Mother, Father God/Goddess, great infinite Spirit, angels, lightworkers, spirit guides, trans-dimensional beings of light, knowing we are all one, and knowing that all we need to do is ask and we shall receive. So, currently, I am asking for your presence, divine Spirit, to fill this space, filling my mind, my body, and my soul - allowing me to be a clear channel of your infinite light, love, wisdom, healing energies,*

*and the Christ consciousness. As I feel your presence, I give
thanks. Welcome! Welcome to all those of the higher realms.
I thank you for your loving, compassionate, and joyful
participation. Today, I thank you Mother Earth, Father
Sun-God for the healing of myself and others and the
healing of Mother Earth. Peace on Earth begins today, and
it begins within me. I accept that I am a divine child of
God. It is safe for me to feel all my feelings. I will release,
relax, and allow Divine Love to enter me. A'ho.*

They instructed me to inhale and begin counting
down from 10. I don't think it was more than three
seconds before I was off traveling the Universe. It was
an intense experience. I lost all awareness of my body.
I felt completely out of control, which was the point –
I had to realize that I was not the body. Bufo is
referred to as the 'God Molecule' because often the
individual who ingests the medicine has an experience
of God, and that was exactly what happened to me. I
experienced my oneness with God. I realized I was
pure awareness, swimming in an infinite ocean of love
that was God. In that place, that state of
consciousness, there was no illness and no judgment.
There was only God.

When I came to, I sat down with Dr. Gerry and
recounted my experience. I asked him if it was
possible to go in again and he obliged.

The second time I went in, the toad went in and
healed lifetimes of pain, guilt, and grief. It showed me

a past incarnation where I had slaughtered people, and it showed me all the visceral pain my family lineage had inflicted on the world. Jesse said I screamed as though I was giving birth. As I screamed, I released everything into the Universe.

That evening as we slept, I felt the continued effects of the medicine and was very aware of the toad's presence in the room. It was as though there was a 20-foot-tall toad standing guard as it continued to heal and clear energetic imprints from my subtle and physical bodies. This continued for a few days. I could also feel Jesus.

At times, I felt as though I was being energetically operated on. Because I was still processing, I wanted to go home without stopping to see my father, but Jesse wouldn't let me get away with that. I figured this would be one of the last times that I'd see my father since he was older and had lived a very hard life. We headed to my father's house so that I could say goodbye.

When we arrived, a weathered-looking man broke down in tears as he saw me and the physical state I was in. I could barely walk.

Thanks to the work the toad had facilitated, I was able to let go of a lifetime of hurt and resentment that I had carried towards my father right in that moment. We reestablished a connection with one another. Since then, I visited my father a couple of times and I feel healed from our past relationship. The toad showed me the only thing that is real is Love, which helped me to release any resentments I once had.

> *I believe the real goal of this medicine is to heal traumatic experiences and release energetic karmic residue and energetic blockages, allowing one to expand fully into one's true energetic state, perceive and experience the fundamental energetic unity of all things life and consciousness, achieve personal clarity into one's true nature and reach liberation from all personal imaginary limitations and ego produced perceptions and fears.*

~ Dr. Gerry Sandoval

KAMBO FROG

Kambo is a traditional medicine used by many of the tribes in the northwestern part of the Amazon rainforest. A waxy poison is collected from the back and sides of the Giant Monkey Tree Frog. The Kambo, a non-psychedelic, is collected from the frog without hurting it and placed on small wooden paddles where it is allowed to dry. Before use, the dried Kambo is reconstituted. Prior to application, the Kambo is formed into the required number of dots, which is determined by your experience and health.

The initial session always involves a strict safety protocol to test your reaction to a tiny amount of Kambo. A thin piece of vine is heated up and the burn points are placed on the arm or leg, producing an instant opening on the skin. It is a tribal tradition for men to receive their Kambo on their arms or chest while women receive theirs on the lower leg. The Kambo points are then applied to the openings and water is applied to help the process of absorption. Prior to receiving the Kambo, it is traditional to drink a large amount of water to balance the alchemical 'fire' energy of Kambo. Each time Kambo is taken, the experience is different. There is no real familiarity even with repeated use. Often, participants report that the Kambo scans his or her body and then seems to focus the healing in areas where it's most needed.

I like working with Kambo because it detoxifies the organs – my kidneys need the additional support due to the IVIg medication.

AYAHUASCA

The work towards enlightenment, or healing, is not always pretty. It requires that the worst and darkest parts within us be brought to the surface and seen. It presents us with an opportunity to be a modern-day alchemist. We get to allow the 'darkness' to rise and be present with it without judgment (By dark I am referring to anything, unlike love.). As we become aware of the dark, we get to choose again. We get to decide and declare who and what we truly are, which is ultimately Love.

I had traveled to a plant medicine retreat center in Guatemala in 2018 in the middle of a healing crisis, and this time, I traveled alone. While at the retreat center, I met with a Mayan shaman for an astrological reading during which he said,

"Don't fear the darkness that shows up in ceremony, it must all come up to be healed. Realize that you alone write your story, and it is time to write a new one."

His words could not have come at a better time as the ceremony we had planned for later that evening was going to bring me face to face with an intense level of darkness.

Once the nighttime settled, the ceremony began. As the hours went by, there was much Mother Ayahuasca showed me. She shared a vision with me that revealed the level of darkness that I assumed belonged to the planet. Somehow, I had managed to trap it and lock it in a cage. It was the size of King Kong. As I sat at the edge of the cage and peered into its terrifying eyes, I realized that the darkness I saw was not of the world, it was mine.

Was it possible that much darkness lived in me?

Apparently so as it was what Mother Aya was showing me. I didn't know what to do and my first thought was to kill the darkness. Almost instantly, I realized that darkness cannot be destroyed, it can only be transmuted.

How was I supposed to go about doing that?

Then I heard Mother Aya say,

"These are all aspects of you that need to be loved back into the fold so your soul may be whole."

This was the beginning of yet another level of self-love and forgiveness.

The work of transmutation has taught me how to hold everything without judgment. I had to recognize that the only reason the darkness was present was to be transmuted as energy can never be destroyed. When we begin to see darkness as an error in thought and not the truth of who and what we are, then we are deep in the alchemical work of transformation. The chemical reaction that ensues transforms our sins or errors in thought. This ultimately results in forgiveness of self and others and ushers in a newfound sense of Self, freedom, and love. It does not matter how long a room has been dark, what matters is that we turn on the light and realize that we are the light.

Chapter 27
Spiritual Practice

"There are only two mistakes one can make along the
road to truth: Not going all the way, and not starting."
~ Buddha

The world of effects is not always easy to
navigate. Through daily spiritual practice,
we are better able to remain in alignment
with what is True. For me, these practices include:

- Meditation
- Affirmative Prayer
- Visioning
- Sacred Service
- Spiritual Study
- Spiritual Community
- Tithing

Our assignment while on this planet is to cultivate and demonstrate the God presence within each of us. Through spiritual practice, we get to participate on a regular basis with the power that governs the entire Universe. Through prayer and meditation, we are reminded of our True nature, that we are eternal and unconditional Love Itself. Turning within allows us to hear rightly the eternal broadcast from Spirit as it is ever guiding and navigating the journey of remembering. These practices assist us to see through the illusion of separation from God and one another, which allows us to see ourselves when we look at the world. From this space, we get to heal our own consciousness and as we are lifted, all are lifted along with us. From this space, we get to live with one foot in this world and one foot in the spiritual. Over time, we become keenly aware that there is one life, and it expresses as Us – each of us being an intricate part of the Whole.

If you ever find yourself tempted to believe that there is not enough time to be still, to pray, or to serve, simply remind yourself how much sweeter life is when in the company of ease and grace. Turning within daily uplifts the consciousness of the entire planet and allows you to ask empowering questions such as

"What would you have me do today, sweet Lord?"

And my personal favorite is,

"…and what will you have me wear?"

Chapter 28
Acceptance

A substantial part of my healing journey has been coming to terms with my parental issues. As much as I love my dad, there is no denying that he wasn't around for much of the journey. I was 14 when my father said something to me that caused a serious wedge between us.

"You are just like your mother."

He didn't mean it as a compliment. In fact, it was about as hurtful a thing as he could say to me at that time. Although my parents divorced when I was 5, I looked at my dad as the more loving of the two and I often defended him when my mother talked down on him. His words comparing me to my mother pierced like a dagger through the heart and what was even worse, I no longer had a single supportive parent in my corner.

My mom was the reason I ran towards spirituality. I needed protection from what felt like terror and evil. I often pictured my mom as one of those animals that eats her litter – and not because she was evil, but because it was in her nature. I think I could have easily healed from my history with my mother had she shifted her behavior at any point. The problem for me was that mom harassed me while I tried to work and support myself. She hated that I attended self-development classes at Agape and had advanced through Practitioner Studies. Her behavior continued as I moved through ministerial studies. For years, I thought my healing was connected to her and resolving our relationship. I thought as a spiritual person, I had to forgive her.

Around the time of my wedding, my mom started to act crazily again. She sent messages to Jesse and would give him reasons why he should not marry me. Thank goodness Jesse had been with me for 10 years so I didn't have to plead or prove my innocence to him.

"Does your mom really think I wouldn't marry you based on something she says?" he asked.

My mom's demonstration around my wedding was how our interactions had been my whole life. My mom would talk badly about me to relatives and friends, only for them to call me and tell me how horrible of a person I was and that I should love my mother. The issue was never that I stopped loving her; she just never behaved lovingly towards me.

A few weeks before the wedding, my son came to visit me in Las Vegas. As we were out having dinner, my mother started to bully me. This time, she accused me of throwing myself at her previous partners and that I was the devil's child. My son looked at me and asked,

"Mom, when is enough *enough*? If you ever did a fraction of what grandmother has done to you to me, we would not have a relationship."

In that moment, I had to decide if enough was enough, and finally, it was. I wanted my mother at my wedding, AND I wanted Jesse and me to be the focus. I knew that if my mother was there, she'd find a way to draw attention to her and away from the sacredness of our day. I didn't want to worry about her rushing me at the altar and attempting to convince a room full of people I was the demon child that she believed me to be. I had to release the guilt of not inviting her.

It has taken me 50 years, but I finally arrived at a place where I knew the calling on my heart was to serve humanity. I may not be able to have a relationship with my mom according to societal standards, but my love for her is unfailing. I love her enough to allow her to be who she is. She is not

responsible for my happiness, I am. If my mother wakes up from the role she is playing before it is time to cross over to the other side, I will greet her with open arms. In the meantime, I will no longer subject myself to physical, mental, or emotional abuse. Our contract is done, and our mission is fulfilled. I had to learn to look at the impact and not the why, which has helped me heal my relationship with my parents tremendously. And this is what I discovered:

1. It feels good to know my well-being is within my control alone and not some outside force, regardless of how anyone behaves.
2. I have access to my groundedness, despite the unease around me.
3. I am not responsible for another's opinion of me. I KNOW WHO I AM.
4. I see through the invitations to engage in unloving ways, and I AM SIMPLY NOT INTERERSTED.
5. I no longer need my parents to change for me to be happy and at peace; as such, I have discovered what it means to be ME, to be free.

One of the questions I ask myself now is,

"If this person/situation never changes, what do I need to do to be happy or at peace?"

This way of being, has allowed me to live from an empowered place. Thank you, mom and dad.

I am here to serve humanity in its awakening. As Dr. Sue mentioned,

"If your parents were not around, it's because you didn't need them. Big souls come in for big lessons and they get started right away."

I realized that I had big lessons and as my life showed and continues to show me, I had to get started right way.

Chapter 29
Conclusion

When I first tried to write this book a couple of years ago, a lot of anger surfaced from deep within me, traveled through my fingers, and splattered onto the screen. I was not healed enough yet to share my story, even from a historical viewpoint. Even with all my anger, I knew it served a purpose. My life was custom-made for me and was a result of my "Bus Stop Conversation." I have reflected often on my life experience and if given the chance to change anything, I wouldn't. I wouldn't want to alter the outcome and I am pleased so far with who I have discovered myself to be.

Although I started back with the IVIg infusions (for now), I wake up grateful each day to be alive. I praise Spirit for how much It loves and supports me. My focus over the past four years shifted from survival to pure joy – the kind of joy that is not dependent on outer circumstances, the kind of joy that is birthed from within. The amount of study and experience this journey has afforded me has allowed me to see the interconnectedness of all of life. I have reached a place within myself where I see beyond the story, the illusion, and the role everyone has played.

I completed ministerial studies successfully in 2020 and my class was the inaugural class of the Michael B. Beckwith School of Ministry. I also successfully completed *The Energy Codes Course Work Levels 1 - 4.5; The Energy Codes Book Facilitator Training; The Energy Codes Trainer Certification Program;* and *The B.E.S.T. Practitioner Training.* I am also now certified as a Spiritual B.E.S.T. Practitioner. I am so glad I didn't give in to my fears and am grateful to every one of my teachers and classmates. Thanks to Rev. Michael, Dr. Sue, and all the amazing ministers and teachers I have encountered along the way, I can say I am a sovereign being and you can't put a price on true freedom. I realize I am a powerful creator who can love unconditionally, forgive, show compassion, and serve as our Master Teacher, Yeshua the Christ, did. Which reminds me, I have one more story to share with you.

A Mystical Encounter

During the summer of 1976, I went to spend a weekend with one of my favorite cousins in Oxnard. My cousin and I lived next door to one another when my Aunt Hilda took her life. After that, he and his family relocated to Ventura, and I missed him. We loved spending time together. We would play fight after binge-watching action movies.

My aunt, his mother, was very religious. She started attending the local Seventh Day Adventist Church after relocating. As we drove from Los Angeles to Oxnard, my aunt led us in singing various church songs. There was a deep sense of normalcy to their family that I longed for. I remember singing "Father Abraham."

Father Abraham had many sons, many sons have Father Abraham, and I am one of them and so are you, so let's just sing along …right arm and so on and so on.

That evening after we arrived at their new home, we watched TV and later went to bed. My aunt and uncle lived modestly in a one-bedroom duplex. The bedroom consisted of their king size bed and a set of bunk beds. I got the bottom bunk, and my cousin David got the top bunk. A few hours into the night, something woke me up. I looked up at the wall space above my aunt and uncle's bed and I saw an image. I rubbed my eyes in disbelief and wanted to make sure I was in fact awake. Above their bed was an image of

177

Jesus (Yeshua) in the middle (his face interchanging with mine) with his mother, Mary, to the right and a serpent to the left. The images moved slightly. I could tell the snake was upright on its tail and Mother Mary watched Yeshua/me intently. This went on for hours. After a while, I thought that if I hid under the blankets, the image would go away. When I pulled the covers off from over my head, the scene on the wall continued. I went back and forth between turning away from it and turning back, but the image remained. This went on all night. The image didn't disappear until the sun rose. As we got ready for church that morning, my aunt asked me if I slept OK. She noticed I tossed and turned all night. After I explained to her what I saw, she made no facial expression nor gave any indication as to whether she believed me.

I had been to my aunt's church once before and I loved it. I enjoyed the children's Bible study and all the songs we got to sing. Before I was allowed to go into the class, my aunt had me share with the pastor what I saw the night before. When I recounted the events, the pastor suggested that I be baptized in the holy water to get rid of any evil that may have been on me. I don't think my aunt liked having me around as much after that.

Because of the religious dogma, I was exposed to, I believed the experience meant I had a 50/50 chance of being good or evil. I tried my best to live a life of righteousness and when I faltered, I figured it was predestined. I saw the snake as the Devil and Mary as the path of light; since I was between the two, it appeared I had a choice to make.

Later in life, I discovered teachings about the Essenes and the Magdalene communities. The teachings they practiced came from the mystery schools of Isis in Egypt as well as from the Grand Masters from the East. Part of their practices focused on working with the kundalini energy to awaken the high brain centers and raise their consciousness. The kundalini energy is represented by the serpent.

What I have gleaned from this memory is that I have been anointed from the beginning. The Christ consciousness within me is what has been seeking to be awakened. The serpent was representative of the energy that must rise within me. Recently, I had a channeling session with a practitioner who channels Mother Mary and she asked me if I had any questions for her. I shared the experience of Yeshua, Mother Mary, and the serpent with her. I wondered if she had any information for me. At that moment, Yeshua walked in with Mary of Magdalene and Quan Yin. Yeshua said that I agreed to come to Earth with the condition that I was not allowed to forget why I was here; the vision that I had was in service to that. Mary Magdalene stepped forward and offered herself as a mentor; Quan Yin and Mother Mary did, too.

I am the light of love and have surrendered the need to contradict this truth about myself any further. My vow to humanity is to assist it in Love as it remembers this Truth about Itself.

In Service to Love,

- Rev. Cynthia

About the Author

I was born in East Los Angeles, California at the beginning of the 70s. I never would have guessed I would become a New Thought Minister or a holistic practitioner. In fact, because of my lack of interest in catechism as a child, it was the last thing I expected I would do but here I am. Becoming a minister and spiritual counselor turned out to be two of the best things I ever did. Add to this my training in energy medicine and I am now what I came here to be. I listen to my clients tell me about their concerns while creating and maintaining a field of love. I work with their energy fields and help them clear subconscious blocks that allow them to embody more of who they really are. I seal it all with prayer affirming what has always been so. That Spirit is our source in all things.

I am also a wife who has a wonderful, loving, and supportive husband. I am a mother and grandmother and now I am a published author. I have discovered what it means to create a life that is truly worth living and I am constantly exploring more of what it means to be me. I have discovered I love humanity and know I am here at the right time. A part of me suspects I was aware of the number of challenges we would go through as a species on the planet and because of that I really wanted to be here to assist usher in a new world. A world that works for all. A world where love becomes the focus and darkness, competition, and greed become a thing of the past. I am incredibly excited for where we are heading and to know deep within my heart that in the end, love wins. I am grateful, that we are returning to our wholeness.

- Cynthia Ambriz

CPSIA information can be obtained
at www.ICGtesting.com
Printed in the USA
JSHW041946181222
35107JS00005B/25